DORSET WILDLIFE

A NATURAL HISTORY OF DORSET

ANDREW MAHON

DORSET BOOKS

First published in 1990 by Dorset Books

Copyright © 1990 Andrew Mahon

ISBN 1 871164-10-9

British Library Cataloguing-in-Publication Data
  Mahon, Andrew
    Dorset wildlife.
    1. Dorset. Natural history
    I. Title
    508.4233

Printed and bound in Great Britain by Penwell Print Ltd, Callington

DORSET BOOKS

Publishing in association with Dorset County Council

An imprint of Wheaton Publishers Ltd
A member of the Maxwell Communication Corporation plc

Wheaton Publishers Ltd
Hennock Road, Exeter, Devon EX2 8RP
Tel: 0392 411131

SALES
Direct sales enquiries to Dorset Books at the address above

For Victoria

who provided the sleepless nights
when so many thoughts came
together.

Acknowledgements

Photographs are reproduced by kind permission of the following:

Durlston Country Park: pp. 54 (Haymeadow), 62 (Guillemots), 63 (Kittiwakes, Samphire)
David Boag: pp. 49 (Dipper), 59 (Trout)
Robert Dickson/Natural Image: pp. 39, 81
Robin Fletcher/Natural Image: p. 17
Bob Gibbons: pp. 45, 53 (Vetch), 59 (Water-lily), 64 (Geese)
Philip Goddard: pp. 29 (Tormentil), 54 (Marbled White), 68
Jean Hall/Natural Image: p. 88 (Shelduck)
Mike Lane/Natural Image: pp. 18 (Stonechat), 61 (Tern), 70
Mike Mockler: pp. 38, 51 (Dartford Warbler, Lizard)
M. W. Richards/RSPB: p. 87
P. Van Groenendael/RSPB: p. 18 (Hobby)
R. Williams/RSPB: p. 64 (Godwit)
Peter Wilson/Natural Image: pp. 53 (Beetle), 57 (Woodpecker), 58 (Kingfisher)
Michael Woods/Natural Image: p. 40

All other photographs by the author

Illustrations by Paul Matthews

Cover photographs: Dartford Warbler (Mike Mockler), Early Spider Orchid and
Great Green Bush-cricket (the author)

CONTENTS

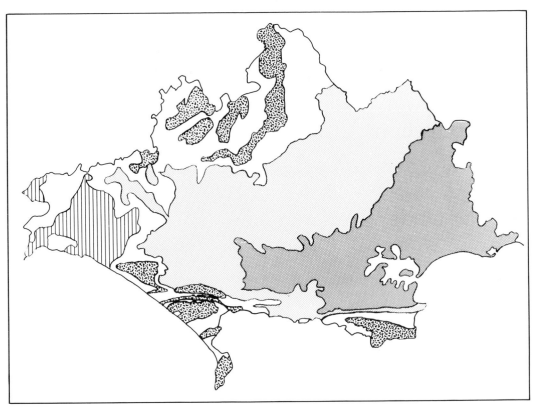

Key to map

'Heathland zone'

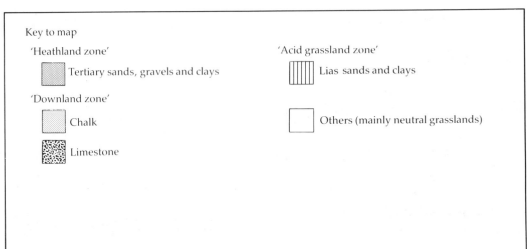

| | Tertiary sands, gravels and clays |

'Downland zone'

Chalk

Limestone

'Acid grassland zone'

Lias sands and clays

Others (mainly neutral grasslands)

ONE
·INTRODUCTION·

A COUNTY OF CONTRASTS

FEW OTHER COUNTIES IN BRITAIN come close to matching Dorset for variety and rarity of wildlife. Statistics reveal that forty-eight species of butterfly regularly breed here, that at least twenty-eight types of wild orchid have been recorded in recent years and that the definitive Dorset list includes 358 birds. Impressive figures indeed, but pure mathematics cannot even begin to reflect the real natural beauty of the countryside, of which the wildlife is an integral part.

Left: Chapman's Pool on the Purbeck coast. Below: The Blackmoor Vale viewed from Batcombe Down.

orset is a county of contrasts, with fertile river valleys, tracts of gorse-studded heathland, rolling chalk hills dissected by deep-cut combes; rich vales with wooded hedgerows enclosing a patchwork of dairy pastures and a diverse coastline of cliff, dune, estuary and shingle. The key to this variety of landscape and habitat is the underlying geology.

The sedimentary rocks of Dorset were formed over hundreds of millions of years. Most were conceived on the ocean bed, but others originated in freshwater lakes or on vast mudflats, as the general sea level rose and fell according to the huge variations in global climate. Then, about twenty-five million years ago, the collision of the two continents of Africa and Europe caused massive upheavals in the earth's crust, contorting the accumulated layers of rock and creating folds, cracks and tilting –

Right: Chalk downland near Melbury Abbas. Below: Winfrith Heath.

often almost to the vertical. The Dorset coastline conveniently slices through this deformed sandwich, to reveal in cross-section the progression from the older Jurassic rocks in the west of the county, through the Cretaceous chalk, to the more recent Tertiary sands, gravels and clays of the Poole Basin.

The contortion of the rock strata, and subsequent erosion by the sea and the weather, brought previously buried layers to the surface. This formed an often intimate and small-scale pattern of parent materials to influence the formation of the soil, and hence the vegetation which is supported. This is why the contrasting habitats of downland and acid heathland occur so closely juxtaposed; most noticeably on the Isle of Purbeck, where two types of alkaline limestones, neutral Wealden clays, alkaline chalk and highly acid Bagshot Beds occur within a distance of less than five kilometres in places.

The different rocks show varying resistance to erosion, so the harder limestones remain as ridges and hills inland and as steep cliffs along the coast, while the much softer clays and sands form the valleys. The range of aspects, slopes and drainage patterns produced are further fundamental influences on the wildlife communities.

Dorset's location on the south coast bestows a relatively warm climate, which favours many plants and animals unable to survive further north. Many insects are at the northern limit of their range here: they are typically associated with the hot micro-climates of open south-facing slopes of downland or heathland. Other species, particularly plants, are at or near the southern or eastern limit of their range. These are the ones which depend on the generally warm, moist

Left: The Purbeck beds exposed in Durlston Bay.
Below: Great Green Bush-cricket.

conditions which occur throughout the year due to the influence of the Atlantic Ocean.

The great diversity of conditions created by this combination of geological, geomorphological and climatic factors naturally leads to a high diversity of wildlife communities. In many parts of Britain, modern farming and development have obliterated the range of semi-natural habitats created by ancient man. Yet Dorset's isolation from major industrial and residential developments – at least until very recently – and the continuation of traditional management have preserved a high proportion of the interest.

Even Dorset is subjected to modern pressures eventually, and special measures are necessary to preserve many of the habitats today. A recognition of the international importance of many of the areas by statutory and voluntary

conservation bodies has led to the designation of many sites as nature reserves. This should ensure the perpetuation of at least a representative area of these anachronistic land uses and their associated communities of plants and animals.

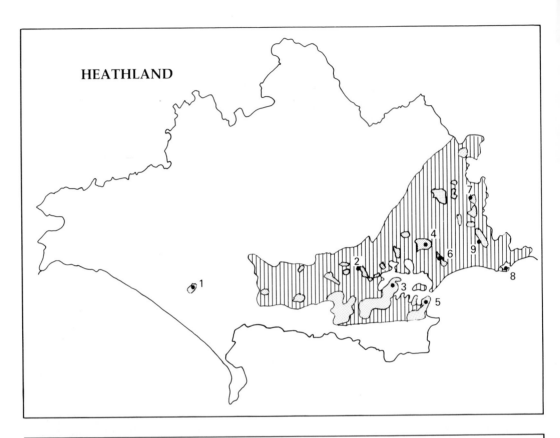

Key to map

▯▯▯ Heathland zone   ▨ Major heathlands   ● Places to visit

Site	Ownership	Special interest
1. Black Down (Hardy Monument)	Private*	Dry heath
2. Wareham Forest	Forestry Commission	Wet heath
3. Arne	RSPB*	Birds, dry heath, reptiles
4. Canford Heath	Private*	Birds, dry heath, reptiles
5. Studland/Godlingston Heath	National Trust/ Nature Conservancy Council	Dragonflies, wet and dry heath, reptiles
6. Bourne Valley	Poole Borough Council	Dry heath, dragonflies
7. Avon Forest Park	Dorset County Council	Dry heath
8. Hengistbury Head	Bournemouth Borough Council	Dry heath, coastal
9. St Catherine's Hill	Christchurch Borough Council/ Private*	Dry heath

* Access restricted to public rights of way and permitted paths

TWO

HEATHLAND

DOMINATED BY THE VAST CARPETS of purple heather blooms, and dotted with the vivid yellow flowers of the gorse, the apparently barren and uniform areas of dwarf shrub vegetation which form the Dorset heathland conceal a surprising variety of plants and animals, including the rare, fascinating and unusual.

Left: Heathland at Avon Forest Park.

The heathlands developed on shallow, acid and infertile soils derived from the Tertiary sands, gravels and clays which form the Poole Basin. Thomas Hardy described how Egdon Heath, a fictitious amalgamation of the vast tracts which still existed in his lifetime, stretched from Dorchester to Poole and Bournemouth, and beyond to the New Forest, broken only by the valleys of the great rivers – the Frome, Piddle, Stour and Avon. Today a little over 5000 hectares of that original 40000 remain, scattered in many hundreds of often isolated fragments. To the west of the county some other small areas of heathland and heathy grassland have developed on poor, acid clay soils, but these generally lack the diversity associated with the 'true' lowland heath of the Poole Basin.

The heathlands are not natural. Pollen, preserved in the depths of bogs which are an integral part of the heathlands, shows that they originated some three thousand to four thousand years ago. Bronze Age man cleared the open, scrubby woodlands which were the natural vegetation of the area. His grazing stock and primitive agriculture, assisted by a deteriorating climate, depleted the meagre store of soil nutrients and caused erosion, creating an inimical environment for tree growth. Dwarf-shrub heathland, better suited for survival under these conditions, became dominant: low-intensity grazing, and the exploitation by a sparse population of the peat, heather, gorse and bracken for low-qualify fuel, ensured the maintenance of Hardy's 'untameable' heath for the next three thousand years.

By contrast twentieth-century farmers, foresters and developers find the heathland less of a problem. Modern technology has been harnessed to convert large areas to provide the food, timber, minerals, houses, roads, factories and shops which a rapidly developing population demands. Poole and Bournemouth have burgeoned at the expense of the heathlands.

Further west and on the Isle of Purbeck, vast areas of regimented alien conifers have replaced the heathers and gorse. While the pressures continue, the majority of the remaining heathlands are variously protected as Sites of Special Scientific Interest and nature reserves, giving some hope for the future.

At first glance, the range of plants and animals on the heathlands seems very restricted and there is little apparent variety to the vegetation. On closer inspection, however, the distribution of the three common heathers betrays an ecological heterogeneity caused by a varying degree of wetness. In very dry areas the Heather or Ling is often joined by Bell Heather. Where the drainage is impeded, or where surface water flows across the ground for much of the year, the Heather is joined or replaced by the Cross-leaved Heath. Each of these zones is characterized by a particular community of plants and animals.

Dry Heath

Few plants can tolerate the extreme conditions which prevail on the dry heath. Most obvious of those which can are the three species of gorse. The large, bushy Common or European Gorse fills warm summer days with its coconut scent. The low Dwarf and Western Gorses are more restricted to heathland, and they neatly demonstrate one of the reasons for the relative richness of the vegetation here. Dorset's geographical location in central southern England provides an overlap between the wildlife communities which are associated with an eastern European (or 'continental') climate, and those which are associated with a western European (or 'oceanic') climate. Hence the Western Gorse is near its eastern limit of distribution in Dorset and the Dwarf Gorse is near its western limit. Paradoxically, the Western Gorse is found more frequently on the heathlands north of Poole Harbour, while the Dwarf Gorse is more typical of the Purbeck heathlands further to the west, as well as dominating in the extreme east as expected. The picture for animals is similar, and with the added advantage of a relatively clement climate on the southern fringe of Britain, the heathlands of Dorset are capable of supporting a richer variety of plants and animals than any other in Europe.

Other plants of the dry heathlands include the grasses Common Bent, Wavy Hair-grass, Bristle Bent and Sheep's Fescue. Few herbs will be found, though pathsides and otherwise disturbed areas sometimes support the diminutive Mossy Stonecrop, Sheep's Sorrel, Heath Bedstraw, Tormentil, Heath Speedwell and Slender St John's Wort. Many of these become more common on areas subjected to repeated burning, when a heathy grassland may develop. Heavily grazed areas may include Yellow Bartsia, Lousewort and Petty Whin.

Local enrichment of soil nutrients causes a different community of plants to replace the typical heathland flora. This is a particularly common occurrence on the more urban

heathlands of Poole and Bournemouth, where tipping of garden refuse or household waste is regrettably all too frequent. Here the Rosebay Willowherb grows, often with Nettle, Yorkshire

Fog, Sheep's Sorrel, Bramble and Ragwort. These ubiquitous 'weed' species are of some wildlife value, but they are a very poor replacement for the specialized heathland fauna.

Heathlands are rich in non-flowering plants. Lichens such as 'Reindeer Lichen', Devil's Matches and other *Cladonia* species are found amongst the heathers. Many, such as *Cladonia gracilis*, are relatively common here but very rare elsewhere. Mosses, though more obvious in wetter areas, also occur on the dry heathland. *Polytrichum piliferum* is typical and others such as *Pleurozium schreberi* and *Hypnum jutlandicum* may also be found. The fern Bracken may often dominate areas of heathland to the exclusion of other plants. Such a situation may reflect a local enrichment of the soil, or areas subjected to repeated burning or disturbance.

With the cessation of exploitation or management of the heathland, natural succession to woodland will occur, though generally only very slowly. Birch, Holly, Alder Buckthorn and Oak may invade, though today these native species are generally joined or replaced by pernicious aliens like Rhododendron and Black Pine, which can very quickly swamp the heathland vegetation and degrade its value as a wildlife habitat.

Left to Right: Cross-leaved Heath, Dwarf Gorse, Dorset Heath, Western Gorse, Bell Heather, Ling. (Top): Common Gorse.

Above: Gorse and Heather flowers. Left: Western Gorse.

Humid and Wet Heath

Wetter areas, where there is a permanently high water table, typically develop a more diverse vegetation than the dry heathland. Purple Moorgrass often dominates, particularly on disturbed or burned humid heathland, and the rare Dorset Heath sometimes grows alongside the typical Cross-leaved Heath, especially in Purbeck. The real interest for the botanist lies in the wet heathland and bogs which develop in and around permanent standing or flowing water. Fascinating insectivorous plants include three species of sundew, Pale Butterwort and several types of submerged bladderwort. Each supplements the meagre mineral nutrients available from the impoverished soils by catching and

Below: Wet heath and bog pool at Godlingston Heath.
Right: The insectivorous Round-leaved Sundew.

digesting small invertebrates. The attractive red globules on the leaves of the sundews are a sticky death trap to an unwary insect.

The tiny Bog Orchid with its curious inverted flowers occurs in a few of the Purbeck bogs. The more widespread Bog Myrtle adds a delicate sweet scent to the air, while the aptly named

Bogbean, Bog Asphodel and the beautiful Marsh Gentian provide a colourful floral foil to the various greens and oranges of the spongy beds and hummocks of *Sphagnum* bog mosses. These may be comprised of nine or ten species, often difficult to distinguish, but including *S. tenellum*, *S. papillosum*, *S. compactum* and the rare *S. pulchrum*. The rare Marsh Club-moss occurs in some of the bogs, often joined by mosses such as *Drepanocladus fluitans* and *Riccardia pinguis*. More obvious plants of the wet heath include Deergrass, Heath Woodrush, White Beak-sedge, and Heath Rush. In the boggiest areas these are sometimes replaced by various species of sedge, Cottongrass, Black Bogrush, Many-stemmed Spike-rush, Bog Pondweeds and the rare Brown Beak-sedge. The humid and wet heathland areas are also under threat of invasion by woody species. Here a cessation of management will encourage the establishment of native willow carr, often accompanied by Rhododendron.

Heathland Fauna

The heathland vegetation supports a rich variety of invertebrate life. Warm, sandy soils of the dry heathland are ideal for the activities of burrowing wasps and bees, such as the striking red and black *Ammophila sabulosa*. Rare flies and beetles abound and nineteen species of ant have been recorded, including the typical *Lasius alienus* and *Tetramorium caespitum*. The latter is often joined by other ant species which live as social parasites, being fed and tended by the workers of *Tetramorium*. The rare *Formica transkaucasica* and *Sifolinia karavajevi* also occur, the former generally in wetter parts of the heathland.

Other less obvious but equally characteristic insects include the Heath Assassin Bug and the Heather Beetle. The latter reaches plague proportions in some years and causes severe defoliation of the heather shoots. The heather also supports sap-sucking bugs. Two butterflies are characteris-

tic of the heathland though neither is confined to it. The Grayling is a species of open, sandy areas where it suns itself on south-facing slopes, wings folded and angled towards the sun to avoid casting a shadow, which might compromise its camouflage. The Silver-studded Blue is regarded as the typical heathland butterfly. In Dorset it

forms discrete sedentary colonies, generally on humid heathland areas where foodplants such as Cross-leaved Heath, Heather, Gorse and Bird's-foot Trefoil grow sparsely amongst the open bare ground required for successful egg laying. The larvae are tended by black ants and the pupae develop within the cells of the ants' nest.

Left: Black Darter on Cross-leaved Heath.
Below: Grayling.

The moth family is very well represented on the heathlands with some eight hundred or so species recorded on and around one of the Purbeck reserves. Some moth caterpillars feed on the Heather itself, most obviously the larvae of the Emperor Moth, the Fox Moth and the Beautiful Yellow Underwing. Less obvious, but much more romantically named, is the caterpillar of the True Lover's Knot. Several species of footman moths, including the rare Speckled Footman, may be encountered, along with the Dingy Mocha, Narrow Bordered Bee Hawk-moth and the Kent Black Arches. The greatest number of species are encountered in areas with a diverse habitat which includes some scrubby woodland.

More than half of the British dragonfly and damselfly species can be found on the Dorset heathlands. All require water for breeding but many stray miles to the drier heathland areas to feed. The Purbeck heathlands support more than twenty species, including the Four-spotted and Scarce Chasers, the Keeled Skimmer, the Common and Black Darters, the Scarce and Southern Aeshnas, the Hairy Dragonfly and the Downy Emerald. Amongst an array of the more delicate damselflies can be found the rare Small Red, Scarce Blue-tailed and Southern Damselflies, often in very good numbers where the habitat conditions are just right.

The Dorset heathlands are justly famous for their grasshoppers. The scarce Bog Bush-cricket occurs in green and brown forms, and is the typical insect of the wet and humid heathlands. Drier sandy areas are home to the widespread Mottled Grasshopper and also the very rare Heath Grasshopper which was discovered as recently as the 1930s. Patches of rushes support the Long-winged Conehead and, near to the coast, the Short-winged, which lay their eggs into the plants' hollow stems. A few of the wettest quaking bogs conceal the now rare but quite spectacular Large Marsh Grasshopper, with its unique popping song which resembles the sound of the exploding gorse seed pods all around. Where heathland grades into scrubby ancient woodland the scarce Woodland Grasshopper is sometimes found.

The commonest predators on the heathland are spiders. Much remains to be learned of their ecology, numbers and distribution but more than two hundred species are regularly recorded. The most obvious are the web-spinners, though the architecture of the vegetation is less than ideal for orb webs. Far more typical are the myriads of glistening hammock webs draped across every gorse bush in the early morning dew. Others, such as the very rare Ladybird Spider, build burrows to trap walking insects. The web-less Jumping and Wolf Spiders actively run down

Right: The very local Heath Grasshopper.

Left: Smooth Snake.

their victims with equal efficiency. The Pink Crab Spider lies camouflaged amongst the heather flowers, waiting for its unsuspecting prey, while the imposing Raft Spider attracts prey by vibrating the surface of boggy pools with its front legs.

The spiders in turn may provide a meal for higher predators, particularly reptiles. All six British species can be found here and the dry heathland of south-east Dorset is the main stronghold of the two rarities: the Sand Lizard and the Smooth Snake. Both are specially protected by law and form part of an intricate food web, which also includes their commoner relatives the Adder, Grass Snake, Common Lizard and Slow-worm. A matrix of wet and dry heathland favours most of the reptiles, and wet heathland is vital for amphibian inhabitants – typically the Palmate Newt and the Toad. Both are quite numerous in the acid waters of boggy areas.

Heathland Birds

The commonest breeding birds of the heathland are the Wren, Meadow Pipit and Skylark, reflecting the paucity of tall vegetation for nesting. These are not the most typical birds, however, and the rare Dartford Warbler and Nightjar are certainly the species most often associated with the heathland. The former is particularly dependent on the heathlands, and it is our only long-term resident warbler. As is typical of a bird on the edge of its range, it is very susceptible to severe winters. It survives them only when having access to a very particular habitat of mature Heather with a proportion of dense Gorse. The nocturnal churring of the Nightjar is a typical summer sound around the less disturbed heathlands and young pine plantations.

Other typical birds are the Stonechat, a well-known but never common breeding species, Yellowhammer, Tree Pipit and Linnet. Green Woodpeckers frequent the ant hills and a few pairs of Redshank, Snipe and the common ducks regularly breed on the coastal fringes of some heathland areas. The declining Woodlark is sometimes encountered on some of the larger

Right: Stonechat.
Below: Hobby.

heathlands, and there are occasional breeding records for the exciting Hobby and very rare Montagu's Harrier. In the winter the related Hen Harrier and the Merlin are frequent and spectacular visitors, but sadly the Red-backed Shrike and Wheatear now appear to have been lost as breeding species.

Visiting the Heathlands

The future of the remnant Dorset heathlands is far from certain. Those protected as nature reserves seem relatively secure, but the pressure for minerals and development on the edge of a rapidly expanding urban area is a continuing threat to the remainder. Planning constraints and Site of Special Scientific Interest status may help, but these do not promote the active management which is vital to prevent degradation and invasion by undesirable species. Nevertheless, an increasing awareness of the conservation value of the heathlands and a heightened public concern for their protection is apparent.

A large proportion of the remaining heathland is owned by the military, and many of the nature reserves have restricted access owing to their fragility or use for research. However a walk across public rights of way at Studland Heath or Canford Heath allows viewing of some of the finest areas, and the excellent RSPB reserve at Arne includes nature trails across parts of perhaps the best managed heathland in Dorset. Other heathland trails are marked from the car parks at Avon Forest Park near St Leonards in the east of the county. The Information Centre here has interesting displays and leaflets about the heathland.

CHECKLIST OF TYPICAL HEATHLAND PLANTS AND ANIMALS

Wildflowers

Common Heather or Ling	*Calluna vulgaris*
Bell Heather	*Erica cinerea*
Cross-leaved Heath	*Erica tetralix*
Dorset Heath	*Erica ciliaris*
Gorse	*Ulex europeaus*
Dwarf Gorse	*Ulex minor*
Western Gorse	*Ulex gallii*
Common Sundew	*Drosera rotundifolia*
Marsh Gentian	*Gentiana pneumonanthe*
Bog Asphodel	*Narthecium ossifragum*

Grasses

Bristle Bent	*Agrostis curtisii*
Purple Moor-grass	*Molinia caerulea*
Wavy Hair-grass	*Deschampsia flexuosa*

Insects

Silver-studded Blue	*Plebejus argus*
Grayling	*Hipparchia semele*
Emperor Moth	*Saturnia pavonia*
Fox Moth	*Macrothylacia rubi*
Heath Grasshopper	*Chorthippus vagans*
Mottled Grasshopper	*Myrmeleotettix maculatus*
Bog Bush-cricket	*Metrioptera brachyptera*
Black Darter	*Sympetrum danae*
Small Red Damselfly	*Ceriagrion tenellum*

Birds

Dartford Warbler	*Sylvia undata*
Stonechat	*Saxicola torquata*

Reptiles

Sand Lizard	*Lacerta agilis*
Smooth Snake	*Coronella austriaca*

Heather or Ling.

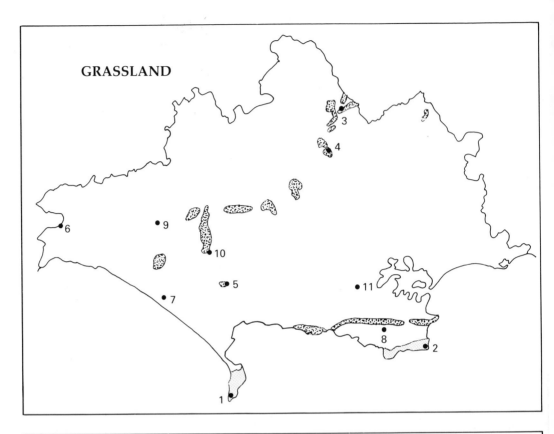

GRASSLAND

Key to map

Location of
major downland areas   ▨ Chalk   ▦ Limestone   ● Places to visit

Downland	Ownership	Main interest
1. Portland	Various*	Plants, butterflies, other insects
2. Durlston Country Park	Dorset County Council	Plants, butterflies, other insects
3. Fontmell and Melbury Downs	National Trust	Plants, butterflies
4. Hod and Hambledon Hills	National Trust/Private*	Plants, butterflies
5. Maiden Castle	English Heritage	Plants
Other Grasslands		
6. Lambert's Castle	National Trust	Plants
7. Abbotsbury Castle	Private*	Plants
8. Corfe Common	National Trust	Plants, insects
9. Kingcombe	Dorset Trust for Nature Conservation	Plants, insects
10. Sydling Meadows	Private*	Plants
11. Wareham Common	Private*	Plants

* Access limited to public rights of way

THREE

GRASSLANDS

FROM THE INTENSIVELY MANAGED RYEGRASS LEY to the apparently natural flower-rich chalk downs, the Dorset grasslands are all products of man's agricultural practices over thousands of years. The wildlife value of these pastures and meadows varies according to the degree of interference from the farmer, as well as more natural factors such as geology and hydrology. In general, the old traditional farming techniques produced high quality habitat but a low level of output. The agricultural revolution and modern pressures to maximize productivity led to a tremendous increase in food production from the land, but nearly always at a cost to its wildlife interest.

Watermeadows in the Sydling Valley.

Extensive tracts of downland once existed on the inland chalk and on the limestones of the coast. The low-intensity grazing of large flocks of sheep, or occasionally herds of cattle, maintained the open landscape, famous for its wildflowers and butterflies. The practice of folding the sheep near the farmstead at night perpetuated the low fertility of the downs and hence the diversity of plants.

Modern chemical fertilizers and farm machinery enabled better use to be made of these lands, and vast areas were ploughed to produce cereal crops and monocultures of agricultural grasses. Sheep grazing is now rarely profitable on the extensive system and remnants of the downlands are largely restricted to steep slopes inaccessible to the tractor and plough. Even here, the cessation of grazing on some parts has led to scrub invasion, a process ultimately as damaging to the downland plants and insects as instant destruction under the plough.

Herb-rich grasslands of the more acid soils to the west of the county have fared little better and are now largely restricted to similar inaccessible situations. Some of the finest remaining examples can be found on scheduled ancient monuments, where legislation to protect the archaeological interest from the plough has, incidentally, also protected the wildflowers and insect life. One or two farms continue to be managed along anachronistic lines and here the conservation organizations have been keen to get involved.

Haymeadows, left to grow up for cutting to produce a winter feed for livestock, also attracted the attentions of the agricultural improvers, so that very few of these incredibly diverse grasslands now survive intact. Modern hay and silage is made from a restricted range of artificially produced grasses, resown on a regular basis and of very little value to wildlife. The traditional riverside watermeadows have suffered worst of all, being flat and hence reasonably simply improved once modern drainage techniques have been employed. Often their former interest is revealed in drainage ditches across or around the fields, but even these now tend to be abandoned in favour of subsurface drains.

Despite these pressures, Dorset retains a higher than average proportion of unimproved grasslands, and the geological diversity of the county is reflected in the composition of the flower-rich swards which survive. The specific interest to the naturalist varies from type to type.

Chalk and Limestone Downland

The list of wildflowers recorded from the chalk of Dorset seems almost endless. Few habitats anywhere can rival the diversity of plant species present in such close juxtaposition. It is not unusual to identify thirty or forty species of flowering plants in a square metre of closely

Right: Green-winged Orchid.

activities of moles and rabbits provide temporary opportunities for the germination of Purging Flax, Centaury and Yellow-wort, and for Felwort, a biennial of the Gentian family.

The chalk is perhaps most famous for its orchids. Pyramidal and Common Spotted Orchid are quite common across the county and the northern chalk in particular supports colonies of Frog and Fragrant Orchids. Green-winged and Early Purple Orchids are widespread and the Autumn Ladies Tresses, Fly Orchid and Greater Butterfly Orchid occur locally. The Musk and Burned-tip Orchids are now known from only a handful of sites. The coastal limestone downlands support the most famous of the Dorset flowers, the Early Spider Orchid. This species, the symbol of the Dorset Trust for Nature Conservation, grows in quite dense colonies on just a few downland fields close to the sea between Durlston and St Aldhelms Heads.

Leguminous plants of the pea family are very well represented in the chalk turf, largely due to their capacity to fix nitrogen from the air, an ability which ameliorates the low availability of this vital nutrient in the soil. Typical species include the Restharrow, a hindrance to many early attempts to improve the downlands by horse-drawn plough, and various vetches including the Horseshoe and Kidney Vetches. These, with the related Bird's-foot Trefoil, are very important larval foodplants of the various species of blue butterfly.

Other well-known flowers of the short turf are the dandelion-like Rough Hawkbit, the Harebell and its more local relative the Clustered Bellflower, Small Scabious, Devil's-bit, Cowslip, Burnet Saxifrage and the confusingly similar Common and Chalk Milkworts. Rarities include the Early English Gentian, an earlier-flowering replica of the much more widespread and frequent Felwort or Autumn Gentian, and the Nottingham Catchfly which can be found in one or two coastal locations on the chalk. Field

grazed turf. The low fertility of the soil, and constant nibbling of grazing stock, prevent coarse species from becoming dominant; the downland plants employ a wide range of strategies, making slightly differing demands on the habitat and so allowing close co-existence.

There are dwarf evergreen woody shrubs such as Wild Thyme and Rock-rose. Squinancywort, Lady's Bedstraw and the rare Bastard Toadflax scramble low across the ground between deep-rooted perennials like Salad Burnet and the rosette-leaved Hoary Plantain and Stemless Thistle, the bane of many a summer picnic. Many of the successful plants show complex adaptations to the heavy grazing and water shortages often occurring on thin soils which form on the chalk. Deep roots, waxy cuticles, narrow leaves, spines and closely appressed or rosette leaves are a few of the more obvious strategies which have evolved to cope with these difficulties.

There are few annuals or biennials, but the bare patches created by sheep tracks or the

Fleawort is equally uncommon but is restricted to the northern chalk. There is in fact a wide variation in the composition of the downland vegetation, with differences not only between the chalk and the limestone, but also within the different areas of chalk across the county. This is not immediately apparent to the casual observer but it can easily be demonstrated by detailed ecological analysis, or by examination of the uneven distribution of the rare flowers.

Above: Chalkhill Blue.

The downlands also support a wide range of grasses. Sheep's and Red Fescue, Meadow Oat-grass, Crested Dog's-tail and Yellow Oat-grass are all major components of the sward; but perhaps the best known and typical downland species is the delicate Quaking Grass. Two sedges, the Spring and Glaucous Sedges, are widespread and the rare Dwarf Sedge also occurs at a few sites.

Local factors which affect the composition of the turf include aspect and slope. The former has a particularly marked effect through the moisture regime. Hot, dry southerly slopes support a markedly different flora from the moister and cooler north-facing turf. Mosses are a particularly important component of the downlands, especially those with a northerly aspect. Species such as *Pseudoscleropodium purum*, *Rhytidiadelphus squarrosum* and *Calliergon cuspidatum* are typical.

The beauty of the downland flowers is rivalled only by the sight of clouds of butterflies on a hot summer's day. The blues, jewels of the downland, are typical, with Common Blues often joined by their rarer relatives the Chalkhill and Adonis Blues. The complicated ecology of these great specialities has only recently been fully unravelled. They are dependent on a warm, short turf, the female usually choosing Horseshoe Vetch overhanging a bare patch of soil on which to lay her eggs. The larvae are tended by ants, normally the Yellow Meadow Ant whose hills are common on undisturbed downland. They may pupate within special cells built by the ants beneath the ground, or on the periphery of the nest. Another member of the family, the Silver-studded Blue, has similar close relationships with black ants. It is much more typical of the humid heathlands of the county, but a distinct race occurs in isolation on the limestone grassland which has developed on the old quarries of Portland.

Despite its name, the Brown Argus is another member of the blues to be found on the downs. The Small Blue may also be encountered where its foodplant, Kidney Vetch, grows in abundance, particularly on the coastal limestone. Another great rarity, the Silver-spotted Skipper, occurs in just a few of the very warmest closely grazed chalk downs in the north-east of the county. The Duke of Burgundy breeds in north Dorset sites where its very particular habitat requirements are maintained, and despite its name the Marsh Fritillary, a beautifully marked and striking butterfly, is possibly increasing its chalk downland range, though it is far from common. The secret to its odd distribution in both marshy areas and dry chalk downland is that its caterpillar foodplant, Devil's-bit, has adapted to grow in both habitats.

Other invertebrates are equally diverse and numerous. More obvious than most are the large, lumbering Bloody-nosed Beetles, harmless vegetarians which feed on the bedstraws but with the ability to emit a startling droplet of blood-like repellent liquid when threatened by a predator. Other leaf-eating beetles are more numerous but rather smaller. Many are brightly coloured, often with a metallic sheen. The Stripe-winged Grasshopper produces the well-known wheezing song of warm summer days on the downs: other familiar but little-studied insects include a number of burrowing bees and solitary wasps.

Many small moths depend on downland plants to sustain their caterpillars. The list includes familiar names like Mother Shipton and Burnet Companion, the adults of both being rather unusually day-flying. Wild Thyme may feed the unimaginatively named Thyme Pug and the Annulet, while one needs to check the alternative scientific name of the food plant Burnet Saxifrage to find the reason for the naming of the Pimpinel Pug.

The legumes, rich in nitrogen, support a particularly wide range of sap-sucking and leaf-eating insects. Amongst the many larvae to be found on the Bird's-foot Trefoil may be the caterpillars of the familiar day-flying Six-spot Burnet Moth, and the wasp-like Six-belted Clearwing. The other decorative day-flyers of the downs are the green Forester moths. The Common Forester is quite widespread but its relative the Cistus Forester is much more local, with a caterpillar totally dependent on Rock-rose for its food.

Restharrow is a favoured foodplant of the much less obvious Bordered Sallow and Marbled Clover caterpillars. Many of the moth larvae are night-feeders, hiding amongst dense tufts of vegetation or in crevices in the soil during the day, to avoid high temperatures and the unwanted attention of potential predators.

The lime-rich soils naturally impart a large amount of calcium to the plants growing in them, and this becomes easily available to any herbivores. The snails are the most obvious beneficiaries of this arrangement, using the freely available mineral to build protective shells. The diversity of species is wide, though many are so small as to make identification difficult without the use of a hand lens. The Round-mouthed Snail is common but unusual as it has an operculum, a permanent structure which can be closed to seal the round opening to the shell: most snails rely on secreted mucus to perform this function. The White-lipped Snail and the Banded Snail are larger, more obvious species

Left: The day-flying 6-spot Burnet Moth.

and the Large Chrysalis Snail is amongst the rarest of the Dorset downland snails.

The presence of large numbers of snails is important for the Glow-worm, a well-known but declining beetle whose eating habits are far less attractive than the familiar glow of the adult females. The larvae grow slowly, taking up to three summers to achieve sufficient maturity for pupation, nourished by meals of externally-digested snails which are turned into a broth-like consistency by the injection of enzymes.

Tracts of open downland have insufficient three-dimensional structure to shelter larger animals. The history of the habitat is, however, inextricably linked with the Rabbit which, until the introduction of myxomatosis in a deliberate attempt to minimize damage to crops, was at least partially responsible for the maintenance of the short turf. This was demonstrated very clearly after the first outbreaks of the disease when large areas flowered profusely for one or two seasons, before natural succession and the progress to taller grassland threatened to swamp the low-growing flowers. Today the Rabbit is quite common once again, but is significant only on a local scale.

The most famous bird of the downlands is now a great rarity. The strange nocturnal Stone Curlew has been all but eliminated from Dorset by ploughing. Some pairs survived for a few years in stony fields of spring-sown crops, but modern cultivars aided by chemical fertilizers grow too quickly for this alternative habitat to be of use to such a very shy and easily-disturbed bird. Other ground-nesters may be present where there is a little cover. Skylark, Quail and Meadow Pipit persist, the numbers of the Pipits rising in winter when large flocks may be encountered. Predators from neighbouring habitats include the Fox and Buzzard, both relying heavily on the Rabbit for food.

The chalk and limestone downland is a very uncertain habitat, totally dependent on constant management for its survival. Even then the tops of the downs are ever changing as the percolating rainfall very slowly but surely leaches the soluble calcium from the upper soil layers, turning them acid. This process leads to the strange situation of acid-loving and lime-loving plants growing side by side; though the ease with which the farmer has reclaimed these level areas for intensive agriculture means that very few good examples remain intact today.

These 'chalk heath' communities are also found on hilltop drift deposits, and are marked by the growth of European Gorse which itself appears to hasten the process of acidification. Associated wildflowers include Heath Speedwell, Tormentil, Heath Grass and Heath Bedstraw, names more familiar in the heathland context: indeed Saw-wort, Lousewort, Foxglove and even Heather are quite commonly found as the soil becomes even more acidic. The mosses change correspondingly. *Dicranum scoparium* and *Pleurozium schreberi* are typical of these acid downland areas. The deep-rooted downland plants, such as Salad Burnet, survive longest amongst the modified turf, their tap roots reaching deep down through the acidic upper soil to reach the lower levels which are still rich in calcium. Some well-established perennials tolerate moderate soil chemistry changes so long as the grazing pressure continues, and Rock-rose in particular may thrive for a period.

Left to right: Creeping Fescue, Meadow Oat-Grass, Creeping Bent, Lesser Cat's-tail, Sweet Vernal Grass, Crested Dog's-tail, Yellow Oat-grass, Quaking Grass.

Chalk and Limestone Grasslands and Scrub

A cessation of grazing leads to profound changes in the composition and structure of the vegetation. Coarse grasses such as Cocksfoot, Upright Brome and Tor Grass dominate the sward, and the small wildflowers are shaded into submission. Taller plants such as Pyramidal Orchid may survive a while but gradually other, more robust species like the Early Purple Orchid, Great Knapweed, Crosswort and Dropwort become the commonest flowers. The absence of grazers also leads to a gradual accumulation of organic matter and nutrients in the soil. Woody species such as Bramble, Blackthorn, Hawthorn, Wayfaring Tree, Dogwood and the native Privet invade, and the associated community of insects and other animals naturally changes too.

The taller grasslands are lacking in many critical larval food plants of the downland butterflies, and they are largely replaced by species with caterpillars which feed on grasses. Common species of the brown family dominate, particularly the Gatekeeper and the Meadow Brown. The confusingly named Marbled White, another brown, is also common in places, especially on the coastal limestone. Other grass feeders include the Wall and the Large and Small Skippers. Along the Purbeck coast, the Lulworth Skipper has increased in numbers locally where Tor Grass has invaded the downland. Other butterflies to be found include the impressive Dark Green Fritillary with caterpillars which feed on violets.

The typical butterfly of overgrown heathy patches on the tops of the downs is the Small Pearl-bordered Fritillary. Where Dwarf and European Gorse have become established, the decorative but inconspicuous Green Hairstreak can be quite common and the scrubby areas host a range of associated insect life. The scrub of the coastal downland is particularly rich, providing a good habitat for several species of bush-cricket including the largest and loudest, the Great Green Bush-cricket.

Scrub also provides shelter for larger animals, so predators such as weasels can be found searching out the many small mammals and nesting birds. Dorset is particularly well placed for attracting summer visitors: a range of birds which includes Whitethroat, Lesser Whitethroat, Nightingale, Willow Warbler, Blackcap, Chiffchaff and Turtle Dove may be found nesting in downland scrub. Resident Stonechat, Yellowhammer and Chaffinch join in a very special dawn chorus.

Below: The declining Small Pearl-bordered Fritillary.

The shade cast by dense pockets of scrub completes the change in other associated plants to create a community quite different from the downland. Lichens such as *Cladonia rangiformis* decorate older branches where scrambling Old Man's Beard, Ivy and Honeysuckle grow. Harts-tongue Fern, Stinking Iris and the Arum Lily are typical understorey plants. In a few coastal localities the rare Cuckoo Pint flourishes in rocky shaded areas.

A matrix of short downland turf, taller grassland and pockets of scrub is perhaps the richest habitat of all, drawing a multitude of species from each of the component parts. Such areas are very few, though the quarried limestone areas of Portland and Purbeck retain some outstanding examples.

Below: Old Man's Beard – the wild Clematis. Below Right: Adder – a common reptile of rough grassland and heathland.

Acid Grasslands

Though by no means as rich as the alkaline downlands, the semi-natural acid grasslands of the west and south-east of the county do hold a fascination for the botanist. Of the wide variety of grasses which comprise the sward Sweet Vernal Grass, Sheep's Fescue and Crested Dog's-tail are well-known and widespread. More specialized species may include Purple Moor-grass, Wavy Hair-grass, Heath Grass and the Common and Bristle Bents.

Pill Sedge and various rushes are also widespread but there are few herbs associated with the dry acid grassland habitat. The low buttercup-like Tormentil is perhaps the most frequent exception; with Heath Bedstraw, Heath Dog-violet, Sheep's-bit, Heath Milkwort and Lousewort occasionally encountered on open, often disturbed areas – particularly in the south-east of the county around the heathlands. Yellow Bartsia is locally common on a few marginal grassland sites on the Purbeck Heaths.

The acid grasslands of West Dorset, less extreme than those of the south-east, support a generally less specialized flora which includes several plants more often associated with woodland conditions. Bracken, Bluebell and Wood Sage are common, and Saw-wort is an attractive addition in some parts. Where scrub is allowed to invade, the ubiquitous European and Western Gorses also begin to invade, accompanied in the most acidic sites by Heather. Typical lichens include *Peltigera polydactyla* and *Usnea flammea*. In at least one coastal site the gorse is host to the rare, parasitic Greater Broomrape.

Damper acid grasslands across the county tend to be rather richer in wildflowers. Ragged Robin and Cuckoo Flower occur widely, often with the more particular Marsh Violet, Marsh Lousewort

and various sedges, notably the Low, Star, Panicled, Carnation and Flea Sedges. Wet flushes and permanently wet grasslands support a diverse flora of familiar plants like Soft Rush, Marsh Bedstraw, Heath and Early Marsh Orchids, Marsh Thistle and Marsh Pennywort, as well as the more localized Great Burnet, Marsh Cinquefoil, Marsh St John's Wort, Pale Butterwort, Lesser Spearwort and Marsh Arrowgrass. Three rarities – the Greater Burnet Saxifrage, Whorled Caraway and Viper's Grass – are known from Purbeck.

Left: Tormentil. Below Left: A flower-rich haymeadow at Durlston Country Park

Haymeadows

Haymeadows share many of the characteristics of their grazed field counterparts so that, for instance, there is an overlap of species between limestone downland and neighbouring unimproved meadows managed for hay cutting. However, the once-a-year cut – as opposed to constant year-round nibbling – favours some species more than others, and it is therefore possible to identify a typical Dorset haymeadow flora.

Calcareous meadows are extremely rich in colourful wildflowers. Meadow Buttercup, Yellow Rattle, Red Clover and Ox-eye Daisy are among the most typical species. Others may include Pepper Saxifrage (an indicator of ancient grassland), Burnet Saxifrage, Pignut and three orchids – the Green-winged, Common Spotted and Early Purple. The early downland flowers survive the annual cut having already set seed: so Cowslip, Rough Hawkbit and Bee Orchid are amongst the flowers common to both sides of the fence. More specialized species of less calcareous meadows include Wild Daffodil, Corky-fruited Water Dropwort, Betony and the strange Adder's-tongue, a tiny and atypical fern.

There is also an overlap of invertebrate life with the grazed grasslands. Brown butterflies abound, particularly the Meadow Brown and Gatekeeper. Small and Large Skippers are common, and the Common Blue will breed in haymeadows which include suitable leguminous foodplants for their caterpillars. Meadow Grasshoppers are the most typical songsters though they, like most of the invertebrates, require some form of refuge around the meadow to survive the attention of predators once the hay has been cut, baled and taken away.

More acidic haymeadows show a diverse range of grasses such as Brown Bent, Sweet Vernal Grass and Meadow Fescue, but rather less in the way of wildflowers. Sneezewort and Bitter Vetch are two specialized species, and in damper meadows the flora may be enriched by Creeping Jenny, Meadow Thistle and Heath Spotted Orchid.

Watermeadows

Many of the flat fields along the great rivers of central Dorset were once intensively managed as watermeadows. Intricate systems of sluices and drains allowed the 'drowner' to flood the meadows during times of frost, to protect the growing points of the meadow grasses: water arising from the chalk is relatively warm all year round. When danger of frost for the day was past, the water could be quickly drained to allow aeration of the soil again. The system had the additional benefit of trapping some of the nutrient-laden silt on the meadows, so maintaining a higher level of fertility. These watermeadows were extensively used for an early bite for dairy cattle each spring.

Very few survive today, though remnants of the ditch systems and even the associated sluice machinery can be seen, especially along the middle reaches of the River Frome. Yellow Iris, Ragged Robin and the early Cuckoo Flower are typical of the watermeadow: of the many decorative grasses the Reed Sweet-grass and Reed Canary Grass are perhaps best-known. The Hairy Sedge is also typical of the habitat. Other flowers may include Fen and Marsh Bedstraws, Greater Bird's-foot Trefoil, Southern Marsh Orchid and two species of Valerian. Vegetated drains often support the fragrant Meadowsweet and Water Mint, Water Speedwell and Lesser Pond Sedge as well as several species of dragonfly, damselfly and amphibians.

Near Wareham the more acidic watermeadows are typified by Reed Sweet-grass. Greater Pond Sedge and Lesser Bulrush. Less common species include Cut Grass and Meadow Rue. The extensive ditch systems here support some sixteen species of dragonfly and damselfly, including the Ruddy Darter. Grasshoppers abound and include the Lesser Marsh Grasshopper in addition to the more widespread Meadow Grasshopper and Common Green Grasshopper.

The life of the watermeadows and the rivers is inextricably linked. Many of the birds and small mammals exchange freely between the two, often using the meadows for feeding or nesting. Grey Wagtails and Moorhen are typical breeding birds and Common Sandpiper, Snipe and Heron are seen at other times. Water Shrew and Water Vole are the most familiar small mammal residents.

Visiting Dorset's Grasslands

Many of the remaining grassland areas are well served with public footpaths, but some are at a considerable distance from the nearest road. On the coast, the prime remaining limestone grasslands at Durlston Country Park are easily accessible, as are the chalk downs further west around Lulworth Cove and Durdle Door. Inland, the chalk downlands of the National Trust at Fontmell and Melbury are amongst the finest, while ancient monuments such as Maiden Castle near Dorchester are rewarding places for botanist and archaeologist alike.

Ancient monuments are also good places to explore for acidic grassland interest. Lambert's Castle in the extreme west of the county and Abbotsbury Castle are both worth a visit; Corfe Common in Purbeck includes a range of acid grassland habitats.

The few remaining haymeadows of wildlife interest are largely managed by the conservation bodies. The Dorset Trust for Nature Conservation's reserve at Kingcombe in West Dorset retains some wonderful unimproved meadows. In the Country Park at Durlston there are some traditional meadows in addition to the limestone downland. Watermeadows can be viewed from the road along the lower Sydling Valley north of Grimstone and at various places nearby along the River Frome. Wareham Common comprises some very rich acidic grasslands along the River Piddle.

CHECKLIST OF TYPICAL GRASSLAND PLANTS AND ANIMALS

1) CHALK AND LIMESTONE

Wildflowers

Horseshoe Vetch	*Hippocrepis comosa*
Stemless Thistle	*Cirsium acaule*
Pyramidal Orchid	*Anacamptis pyramidalis*
Salad Burnet	*Sanguisorba minor*
Milkwort	*Polygala vulgaris*
Quaking Grass	*Briza media*
Hoary Plantain	*Plantago media*

Insects

Brown Argus	*Aricia agestis*
Chalkhill Blue	*Lysandra coridon*
Stripe-winged Grasshopper	*Stenobothrus lineatus*
Bloody-nosed Beetle	*Timarcha tenebricosa*

Birds

Skylark	*Alauda arvensis*
Meadow Pipit	*Anthus pratensis*

2) NEUTRAL AND ACID GRASSLANDS

Wildflowers

Tormentil	*Potentilla erecta*
Heath Speedwell	*Veronica officinalis*
Saw-wort	*Serratula tinctoria*

Insects

Common Green Grasshopper	*Omocestus viridulus*
Small Heath	*Coenonympha pamphilus*

3) HAYMEADOWS

Wildflowers

Ox-eye Daisy	*Leucanthemum vulgare*
Yellow Rattle	*Rhinanthus minor*
Cowslip	*Primula veris*
Pepper Saxifrage	*Silaum silaus*

Insects

Meadow Brown	*Maniola jurtina*
Large Skipper	*Ochlodes venatus*

4) WATERMEADOWS

Wildflowers

Ragged Robin	*Lychnis flos-cuculi*
Greater Bird's-foot Trefoil	*Lotus uliginosus*
Cuckoo Flower	*Cardamine pratensis*
Meadowsweet	*Filipendula ulmaria*

Below: Lesser Marsh Grasshopper.

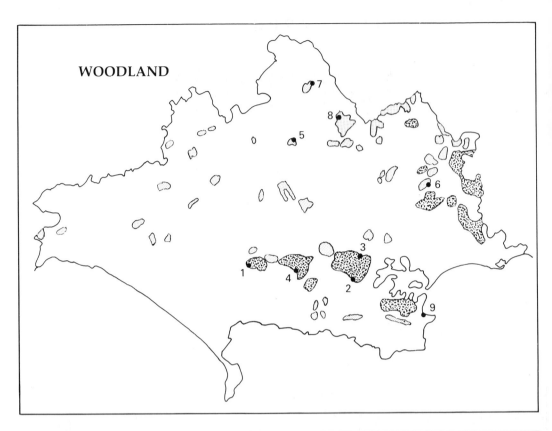

WOODLAND

Key to map

▢ Main blocks of ancient woodland ▨ Main conifer plantations • Places to visit

Site	Woodland type	Ownership	Main interest
1. Thorncombe Wood	Deciduous	Dorset County Council	Birds
2. Sika Trail, Wareham Forest	Coniferous	Forestry Commission	Mammals
3. Sherford Bridge	Deciduous/coniferous	Forestry Commission/Private*	Birds
4. Oakers Wood	Deciduous	Private*	Plants
5. Piddles Wood	Deciduous	Private*/Dorset Trust for Nature Conservation	Plants
6. Holt Woods	Deciduous/coniferous	Forestry Commission/Private*	Plants, birds
7. Duncliffe Wood	Deciduous	Woodland Trust	Plants, birds
8. Littlecombe Wood	Mixed	Woodland Trust	Plants
9. Studland Woodland Trail	Deciduous	National Trust/ Nature Conservancy Council*	Plants, insects

* Access limited to public rights of way

FOUR

WOODLAND

WOODLANDS OCCUPY NEARLY 10 PER CENT OF THE AREA of Dorset or some 25000 hectares, quite a modest total compared with other southern counties of Britain. Little or no truly natural forest remains; but 34 per cent has been designated ancient semi-natural woodland, defined as that which has borne trees since at least 1600. These are the areas of greatest interest to naturalists. They are generally far superior in numbers and variety of wildlife to the remaining plantations, many of which are of exotic conifers.

Left: West Dorset
Bluebell woods.

The total woodland area has actually increased in recent decades, but this is mainly due to the establishment of pine plantations: the figures mask a decline in broadleaf woodland. Most serious from the conservationist's point of view is the loss of coppice woodland, famed for its wildflowers and butterflies but now a rather anachronistic land use which presents landowners with little opportunity for profit. Small pockets remain but, as with the broadleaved woodlands generally, they are usually fragmented, scattered and hence rather isolated.

The major commercial forest blocks have been planted to the east of the county on Cranborne Chase and the acid Tertiary soils of the Poole Basin. Often established on former heathlands, the exotic conifers produce a utilizable timber crop (though sometimes at a marginal profit at best). The scattered broadleaved and mixed woods can be found mainly in the heart and west of Dorset. Concentrations occur on the northern face of the chalk upland, generally on the steepest uncultivable slopes, and in the Blackmoor Vale, where trees in small clumps and along hedgerows add to a well-wooded appearance.

Woodlands of the Acid Soils

The nature of the woods varies according to environmental factors such as drainage, aspect and underlying geology. The acid woodlands of West Dorset are typified by Pedunculate Oak and Downy Birch, with Alder, Sallow and Aspen common in the wetter areas. The most frequent understorey of Holly, Hazel and Guelder Rose is occasionally enriched by the presence of Wild Service and Alder Buckthorn, both important species for wildlife.

The rich groundflora of these woodlands is at its glorious best in spring, before the leaves on the trees eliminate much of the light from the woodland floor. Carpets of Bluebells combine with patches of Wood Anemone, Red Campion and Common Violet to make a colourful display. Yellow Archangel and Primrose add a dramatic contrast of form and colour, while the less ostentatious Sanicle, Herb Paris and Moschatel flower shyly in some areas of the older woodlands. Common Cow-wheat occurs locally, and the popular woodland orchids include Greater Butterfly Orchid, the curious Bird's-nest Orchid and several helleborines, including the rare Violet and Narrow-lipped Helleborines in just a few of the woods. More light encourages Creeping Soft-grass, Pignut, Tutsan and the very local Narrow-leaved Lungwort.

Moist woodlands are often carpeted with other plants such as the Pendulous and Tussock Sedges and the Opposite-leaved Golden Saxifrage, a particular speciality of wet woodlands in the west of the county. Damp heathy copses in

Right: Bugle – a common flower of damp broadleaved woodland.

WOODLAND

the south-east are a stronghold of the now rather rare Royal Fern and the bog moss *Sphagnum fimbriatum*: the ancient woodlands are justly famous for their array of lesser-known, non-flowering plants. Typical woodland mosses include *Mnium hornum, Dicranum scoparium* and the local *Dicranum majus*. Bracken, Lady Fern, Male Fern and two species of Shield Fern are amongst the ferns which survive in the shade of the woods, but perhaps the greatest interest is in the vast array of lichens which grow as epiphytes on trees, particularly those in the ancient parklands and wood pastures.

Much remains to be learned about the numbers and variety of lichens in the woodlands, but identification is difficult. A pollution-free atmosphere, an oceanic type of climate and the retention of very old trees combine to create ideal conditions for the development of the slow-growing lichen flora: over 250 species have been identified in one of the parklands. Familiar species such as the orange *Xanthorias* occur in most areas, but there are also many more local and specialized lichen communities. The unmistakable Tree Lungwort is widespread, and can be quite luxuriant in the medieval wood pastures of Dorset. It is the main species in a typical community which also includes the encrusting *Lecanactis amylacea* and the greyish-yellow *Sticta limbata*.

The nitrogen-rich bark of trees such as Ash, Sycamore, Hawthorn and Field Maple supports a totally different community, including the tufted yellow branches of *Teloschistes flavicans* and the commoner *Anaptychia ciliaris*. Unlike the more common lichens these are seldom found on stones. Smooth acid bark, such as that of the Birch, is often colonized by the Letter Lichens, notably *Graphis* and *Enterographa*. These encrusting lichens form black-streaked, mosaic-like patterns over quite extensive areas of the tree. Unshaded oaks support the common foliose *Parmelia* lichens, a large genus with many representatives in Dorset woodlands. These include the widespread *P. glabratula* and *P. sulcata*, the brown *P. subaurifera* and the more local *P. reddenda*, typically found on the Field Maple and one of many species accepted as being reliably indicative of an ancient woodland.

The so-called Beard Mosses, actually intricately branched filamentous lichens, are typical of acid barks on trees in open situations. The festoons which cascade from some older tree branches include the common, such as *Usnea subfloridana*, and the rare, like *U. articulata*: many of the thirty British species occur in the ancient woodlands of Dorset.

Left: Moschatel.

Left to right: Tree Lungwort, "Beard Moss", Letter Lichen (Graphis Elegans).

Woodlands of the Chalk and Limestone

On neutral or more alkaline soils the character of the woodland changes. The more typical trees here are the Ash and Hazel, with Pedunculate Oak, Whitebeam and Field Maple also common. Small-leaved Lime and Yew are encountered, the latter most notably at the Yew wood of Hambledon Hill, and the former in the woodlands of Cranborne Chase. The generally species-rich understorey may include Wild Privet, Dogwood, Hawthorn, Blackthorn and, particularly on the northern chalk, the Spindle.

Below: Greater Stitchwort.
Right: Ramsons – Wild garlic.
Below right:
Hartstongue fern.

may include the common Early Purple Orchid and the unobtrusive Fly Orchid in more open areas. Ramsons add an overwhelming fragrance of garlic to many of the woodlands in early summer, often growing in huge swathes alongside Cuckoo Pint (or Lords and Ladies). Pendulous Sedge is typical of damp flushes and other wet shady areas.

The groundflora of neutral and chalky soils includes Bluebells, Barren Strawberry, Wood Sorrel and possibly Wood Spurge, Woodruff and Orpine in ancient semi-natural woods. The aptly named Stinking Iris, Great Woodrush and Wood False-brome are also widespread, and the leafless, parasitic Toothwort is occasionally encountered, particularly in association with Hazel. Dog's Mercury often dominates the woodland floor, even in heavily shaded parts, and orchids

Amongst a rich assemblage of non-flowering plants, the striking Hartstongue Fern can be found alongside a variety of mosses including *Polytrichum formosum* and *Dicranum scoparium*. Many of the coppice areas include ancient standard trees which support a rich lichen flora, and there are many specialized relationships between the lichen and the host, such as *Stenocybe septata* on Holly and *Thelotrema lepadinum* on old Hazel coppice.

Woodland Animals

Woodlands probably support a richer variety of animal life than any other British habitat. In summer the still air is alive with the hum of countless hover-flies dancing in shafts of sunlight, while the caterpillars of a tremendous variety of moths do their best to defoliate the trees above. The White Admiral is the most typical woodland butterfly around acid soils, and

Left: Speckled Wood.

open woods throughout the county may still hold colonies of the declining Pearl Bordered, Small Pearl Bordered and Silver Washed Fritillaries. However the rare Wood White is now confined to the west of the county. Thirty-eight species of butterfly breed in Dorset's woods but only thirteen are truly dependent on the habitat. The Speckled Wood is by far the commonest and most widespread. Colonies of the rarer species are more scattered, though nevertheless extremely important on a national scale. The White-letter Hairstreak may now be extinct due to the demise of the elms, but the elusive Purple Hairstreak is still quite common, though seldom seen.

The high canopy is home to the Oak Bush-

Right: Wood Warbler.

cricket, a striking and highly carnivorous lime-green relative of the grasshoppers, which communicates by rapidly drumming its rear feet on a leaf; it lacks the more usual file and scraper mechanism of the family. The increasingly rare Woodland Grasshopper is found at several locations in south-east Dorset on sites where woodland and heathland merge.

The complex web of life in the leaf litter includes the decomposers which facilitate the vital nutrient-cycling process. A bewildering variety of fungi, woodlice, centipedes, millipedes and beetles can be found, more particularly in woodlands where a proportion of dead wood is allowed to remain.

The voices of the Nightingale, Redstart and Wood Warbler may swell the dawn chorus of the already deafening community of common nesting birds in many of the larger woods, particu-larly where there is a good diversity of tree ages. Summer visitors to Dorset woodlands include the Willow Warbler and Chiffchaff, almost indistinguishable to the eye but with very different songs. Great, Blue, Long-tailed, Marsh and Willow Tits may be found all year round, together with the acrobatic trunk-climbing Tree-creeper and Nuthatch. The ubiquitous Magpie is common, and its less well-known but equally splendid cousin the Jay is typical of Oak woodland.

All three species of woodpecker breed here along with the exciting Sparrowhawk and majestic Buzzard. Small mammals such as the Common Shrew, Bank Vole and Woodmouse abound, though the Badger and Roe and Fallow Deer are generally more obvious. By night, the role of insectivore is taken by bats such as the Pipistrelle and Noctule, and the part of the hunter by the Tawny Owl.

Left: Nesting Sparrowhawk.

Right: Dormouse.

Coppice

Specialities of the Hazel coppice woodlands include the Dormouse and a range of common and rare butterflies. These include the Duke of Burgundy, Wood White, Holly Blue, Orange Tip, Comma, Ringlet and Brown Hairstreak, the latter also extending its colonies along adjacent hedgerows. Dormice are shy nocturnal creatures and therefore seldom seen. Signs of their presence are much more common, and include discarded hazelnuts with a neatly chiselled hole through which the kernel has been extracted, and the nest – a loosely constructed ball of leaves, grass and, characteristically, shredded Honeysuckle bark.

Conifer Plantation

Plantations of exotic conifers are generally rather poor in wildlife. Mature pines support a restricted range of birds including the Goldcrest and Coal Tit. The scattered pines of Brownsea and Furzey Islands in Poole Harbour still retain colonies of the native Red Squirrel, elsewhere apparently ousted by its introduced grey relative. The commonest large mammal is another foreigner, the Sika Deer.

Open conifer woodland, typically formed as a result of pines self-seeding into unmanaged heathland, may support remnants of the former community. Large hills of the Wood Ant, comprised mainly of pine needles, are typical of this situation. One insect which has benefited is the Pine Hawk-moth, formerly rare but now common over much of the county.

The shelter provided by young plantations on the heathlands at first increases the potential for ground-nesting birds such as Skylark, Meadow Pipit and the rarer Nightjar, but this value is totally lost as the trees mature. Within a few years there is insufficient light to support a groundflora, and the sterilization of the wildlife-rich habitat which formerly occurred is complete.

Visiting the Woodlands

Many of the Forestry Commission woodlands in Dorset are open for visitors, though few are of great value for woodland wildlife, being mainly modern plantations. The Sika Trail at Wareham Forest offers a good opportunity to see the deer which gave it its name and the Commission offices will provide details of other walks. Thorncombe Wood, near Hardy's Cottage a few miles east of Dorchester, is a pleasant mixed woodland owned and managed by Dorset County Council. Trail leaflets are available.

Elsewhere access is mainly via public footpath and a wide range of woodlands are available by this route. Oakers Wood near Affpuddle, Piddles Wood at Sturminster Newton and Holt Wood are all well worth a visit in the spring or summer, as is the Woodland Trail at the Studland National Nature Reserve. The Woodland Trust now owns several prime sites in North Dorset and produces leaflets to help visitors to enjoy the wealth of woodland wildlife to be found within them.

CHECKLIST OF TYPICAL ANCIENT SEMI-NATURAL WOODLAND PLANTS AND ANIMALS

Trees and Shrubs

Pedunculate Oak	*Quercus robur*
Ash	*Fraxinus excelsior*
Hazel	*Corylus avellana*
Small-leaved Lime	*Tilia cordata*
Wild Service Tree	*Sorbus torminalis*

Wildflowers

Moschatel	*Adoxa moschatellina*
Sanicle	*Sanicula europaea*
Barren Strawberry	*Potentilla sterilis*
Wood Spurge	*Euphorbia amygdaloides*
Dog's Mercury	*Mercurialis perennis*
Bluebell	*Hyacinthoides non-scriptus*
Yellow Archangel	*Lamiastrum galeobdolon*
Ramsons	*Allium ursinum*

Lichens

Beard Moss	*Usnea subfloridana*
Tree Lungwort	*Lobaria pulmonaria*

Ferns

Hartstongue	*Phyllitis scolopendrium*

Insects

Speckled Wood	*Pararge aegeria*
White Admiral	*Limenitis camilla*
Purple Hairstreak	*Quercusia quercus*
Oak Bush-cricket	*Meconema thalassinum*

Birds

Great Spotted Woodpecker	*Dendrocopos major*
Lesser Spotted Woodpecker	*Dendrocopos minor*
Sparrowhawk	*Accipiter nisus*
Tawny Owl	*Strix aluco*
Wood Warbler	*Phylloscopus sibilatrix*

Mammals

Badger	*Meles meles*
Roe Deer	*Capreolus capreolus*
Woodmouse	*Apodemus sylvaticus*

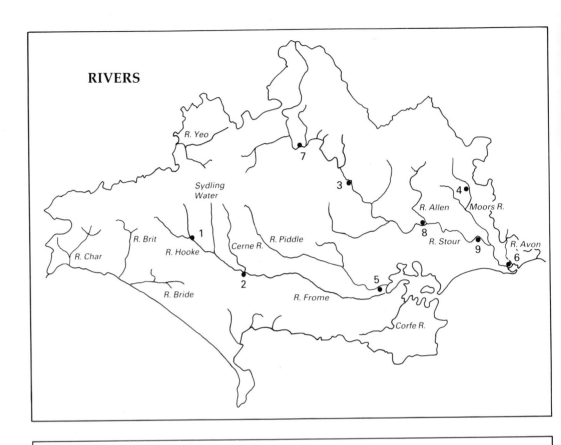

RIVERS

R. Yeo

Sydling Water

R. Brit

R. Char

R. Hooke

Cerne R.

R. Piddle

R. Bride

R. Frome

Corfe R.

R. Allen

Moors R.

R. Stour

R. Avon

Key to map

⌐⊿⌐ Major rivers

Main centres for riverside walks   *Main interest*

Main centres for riverside walks		Main interest
1. Maiden Newton	(Frome, Hooke)	Plants, birds
2. Dorchester	(Frome)	Plants
3. Blandford	(Stour)	Plants, insects
4. Moors Valley Country Park	(Crane)	Plants, insects
5. Wareham	(Frome, Piddle)	Plants, birds
6. Christchurch	(Avon, Stour)	Fish, plants
7. Sturminster Newton	(Stour)	Plants
8. Wimborne	(Stour)	Plants
9. Throop Mill	(Stour)	Plants

FIVE

RIVERS

BEING A RELATIVELY UNDEVELOPED AND UNSPOILED county with a diverse geology, Dorset is blessed with a good number of clean and exceedingly rich rivers. From the almost painfully acidic ditches draining the Bagshot Beds of the south-east to the fine, clear alkaline chalk streams flowing from the central downlands, each water-course has its own character and association of plants and insects.

Left: The River Frome near Woodsford.

The pattern of drainage in the county is such that nature has also provided opportunities for a meeting and mixing of the various waters. Thus within a small area typical acid and alkaline communities converge and compete. Some species survive the full range of conditions. Others are specialized and characterize the favoured portion of the river system. The new habitat created by the confluence also supports some species not found in either parent stream. Add a variation in flow and a drying out of some stretches in the summer, and you have a recipe for a fantastic variety for the freshwater naturalist – and fisherman – to explore.

The Diversity of Waters

Below: Throop Mill: one of many on the River Stour.

Most of Dorset's major rivers originate on the chalk uplands, a major aquifer which acts like a giant sponge. Only the upper reaches of the

system tend to run dry in the summer. Autumn and winter rains quickly recharge the aquifer and the streams flow once again – hence the name 'Winterborne' which has been prefixed to many Dorset villages along these part-time streams. Lower down, reliable springs arise where the chalk sponge is full to capacity. These issue clear, oxygen-rich water which is at a more-or-less constant temperature all the year round. Furthermore, the permeability of the chalk has a moderating effect on the flow: heavy rain is quickly mopped up and released slowly over time through the springs. Such conditions support abundant water plants and insects. The Rivers Frome, Allen and Piddle are prime examples of chalk streams in their upper reaches.

By contrast, Dorset's other great river, the Stour, rises on the upper Jurassic clays of the Blackmoor Vale, taking some minor tributaries from the chalk scarp. This impermeable substrate cannot absorb water like the chalk, and surface run-off causes rapid changes in flow after heavy rain. This creates problems for river wildlife which in general shows adaptations to a particular water velocity: few species can cope with the frequent changes. Submerged plants are particularly inconvenienced by the ever-changing river bed. Fine silty sediment accumulates in times of gentle flow but is quickly washed away during floods, changing the rooting environment and creating such murky conditions that light is unable to penetrate to the plants' leaves. As a result the Stour is generally not quite so rich as the chalk streams.

The drainage from the Tertiary deposits of the south-east of the county is generally acidic in nature. Locally, some of the smaller tributaries such as Uddens Water may show a highly acidic pH of less than four. Few plants or animals can live in such a hostile environment. Those which do are generally specialized and quite rare species. Mixing with tributaries from less extreme origins rapidly ameliorates the acidity, however, and very rich habitats are formed. The Moors River, for example, a confluence of several tributaries of diverse origin, supports an extremely rich assemblage of invertebrates.

Man's Influence

The wildlife to be found in any particular stretch of river results not only from the natural water quality – its chemical and physical features – but also from the degree of use and abuse by man. Rivers suffer perhaps more than any other habitat from pollution; ironically their biological sensitivity is such that they provide us with immediate and obvious indications of these problems. Gross pollution is followed by wide-scale and total death of fish stocks and even minor alterations to water quality can provoke changes. The last British station of the Orange-spotted Emerald Dragonfly was lost when a sewage treatment works was opened on the Moors River, despite the fact that the effluent was well within the accepted standards. Happily the situation in Dorset is amongst the cleanest in the lowlands and there are always promises of improvements even here.

Abstraction, weed-cutting, sluices, dams, fish farms and watercress beds all add their own influence. The removal, return and temporary damming of the waters can all affect the quality of the river and the life which it supports. The unusually large number of weirs, mills and dams on the River Stour has led to the creation of ideal breeding conditions for a particularly notorious species of Blackfly known locally as the Bland-ford Fly. The female's requirement for a blood feed is more often than not fulfilled by obliging Dorset residents and visitors, leaving painful and persistent wounds on their lower legs.

Chalk Streams

A wealth of plant species can be found growing in Dorset's chalk streams, the most typical being the various pondweeds and crowfoots. The latter are a good indicator of regular cutting of submerged vegetation for the benefit of fishermen. Water Starwort and Water Dropwort are also common. Along the margins Water Speedwell, Water Mint and Sweet-grass provide a profusion of summer colour, complemented on the banks by Yellow Iris, Water Forget-me-not, Fleabane and Valerian.

Wild Watercress is a particularly good plant for invertebrates and it supports dense populations of Water Shrimp and non-biting midge larvae. The hundreds of other species of invertebrates which live on water plants and the river bed include snails, worms, water beetles, caddis flies and the ephemeral mayflies. These in turn are a rich harvest for the fish for which the chalk streams are so famous. The rights to Trout and Salmon fishing are jealously guarded and other temptations for the angler include Roach, Dace and Grayling, particularly in the rivers' upper and middle reaches. Less obvious to the fisherman but of equal importance to the ecology of the rivers, the smaller Three-spined Stickleback, Minnow and Bullhead are all numerous.

Left: Water Speedwell.

Right: Dipper.

The Moorhen and Mallard are the commonest river birds and the Mute Swan, Kingfisher and Pied and Grey Wagtails are all widespread. Herons feed along the more sluggish lower reaches of most of the rivers, while in the west of the county fast-flowing gravelly rivers support the Dipper. This is perhaps the most famous and highly adapted river bird, right on the edge of its more usual upland range in Dorset but nevertheless reaching quite good populations after a series of clement winters. The rivers also attract large flocks of Swallows and Martins to feed on emerging insects, and waders such as Snipe and Common Sandpiper feed on the marshy margins.

The most famous river mammal, the Otter, is unfortunately a rarity in Dorset, though occasional records along the Frome and the Stour in particular suggest that there is always a chance of a sighting. Other mammals include the Water Shrew and the Water Vole, both quite common in sluggish stretches and particularly around the watercress beds.

Man's influence on the chalk streams includes watermeadow systems, watercress beds and fish farming. In addition to the artificial stocking of the rivers with Brown and Rainbow Trout there are numerous specialist farms which raise amongst others, Salmon, Carp, Trout and exotic ornamental fish. Native and introduced species of Crayfish – diminutive freshwater relatives of the Lobster – are also cultivated in places. Many of the native wildlife species are considered serious pests: few fish farmers welcome the close attentions of Heron, Otter or Kingfisher, though the latter at least is more likely to be interested in the local Minnows and Bullheads. Plant-eating water invertebrates are a problem for the watercress farmer, though at least here the insect diet of the Wagtails means they are welcome visitors.

Acid Waters

The acid streams of south-east Dorset, flowing through the heathland area, are particularly noted for their rich dragonfly fauna and a survey in the late 1970s recorded some twenty-nine species in the catchment of the Moors River. Even the most acidic waters support the larvae of the Four-spotted Chaser and the Large

Right: Moors River.

Red Damselfly (two species which accompany several others in more moderate water conditions). The Scarce Chaser is a speciality which breeds in the river itself, along with the Golden-ringed Dragonfly and the Demoiselle and Banded Agrions. Other species breed in still waters associated with the river, and can be seen flying nearby.

The higher reaches of these acidic streams tend to dry out in mid-summer and are generally poor in wildlife. Opportunistic and hardy insects such as water beetles and fly larvae can be quite common, but the diversity is low. More reliable reaches often support good numbers of a variety of mayflies and caddis flies, but it is the middle and lower reaches – where the acidity has been diluted by less extreme tributaries – which support the greatest variety of wildlife. Flatworms, watersnails, mussels, leeches, water lice, stoneflies, true flies and water bugs abound

on the river bed, also on the flourishing growth of water plants, which includes several local and unusual species like Fennel Pondweed and the hybrid between Broad-leaved and Shining Pondweeds.

Below left: The rare Southern Damselfly: found along a few of the smaller muddy streams of south-east Dorset.
Left: Demoiselle Agrion.

Visiting the Rivers

Most of Dorset's rivers are accessible along public footpaths, often from villages and towns. Pleasant walks in Dorchester follow the Frome, while in the lower reaches, walks from Wareham allow visits to both this river and the Piddle. Other chalk streams well worth a visit include the upper Piddle and the Cerne, both followed for much of their length by pathways. One river valley to the west, Sydling Water, runs alongside a minor road and at one point retains a ford giving direct vehicular access to the river! The Stour can be visited at Sturminster Newton, Blandford, Wimborne and Throop Mill to the north of Bournemouth. Footpaths and open spaces at Christchurch follow both the Stour and the Avon. Moors Valley Country Park at Ashley Heath includes fine riverside walks along the River Crane, the main source for the Moors River.

CHECKLIST OF TYPICAL RIVER PLANTS AND ANIMALS

Wildflowers

River Water-crowfoot	*Ranunculus fluitans*
Pondweeds	*Potomogeton natans*
	P. perfoliatus
Water Starworts	*Callitriche platycarpa*
	C. stagnalis
Watercress	*Rorippa nasturtium-officinale*
River Water-dropwort	*Oenanthe fluviatilis*

Insects

Demoiselle Agrion	*Calopteryx virgo*
Banded Agrion	*C. splendens*

Birds

Kingfisher	*Alcedo atthis*
Moorhen	*Gallinula chloropus*
Grey Wagtail	*Motacilla cinerea*
Dipper	*Cinclus cinclus*

Fish

Brown Trout	*Salmo trutta*
Roach	*Rutilus rutilus*
Dace	*Leuciscus leuciscus*
Grayling	*Thymallus thymallus*

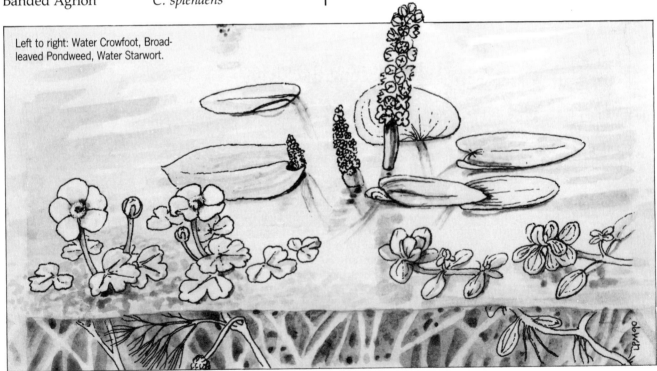

Left to right: Water Crowfoot, Broad-leaved Pondweed, Water Starwort.

DORSET WILDLIFE

Few places in Britain come close to matching Dorset for variety and rarity of wildlife. The spectacular scenery comprises a wide range of habitats which reflect the influence of geology, man and a warm south-coast climate.

HEATHLAND

The very special wildlife of Dorset's most famous habitat includes Dorset Heath
and the beautiful Marsh Gentian. Dry heath is home to rare Sand Lizards and the elusive
Dartford Warbler, while Silver-studded Blue butterflies and a variety of dragonflies,
such as the striking Four-spotted Chaser, live mainly in wetter parts.

Above: Marsh Gentian
Right: Dorset Heath
Below: Silver-studded Blue

Four-spotted Chaser

51

Above: Sand Lizard
Left: Dartford Warbler

Adonis Blue

GRASSLAND

The flower-rich chalk downlands are famous for their colonies of rare Adonis Blue butterflies and other insects like the lumbering Bloody-nosed Beetle. Coastal limestone downs boast colourful displays of Pyramidal Orchid, Horseshoe Vetch and the fascinating Early Spider Orchid.

Early Spider Orchid

Above: Pyramidal Orchid
Left: Horseshoe Vetch
Below: Bloody-nosed Beetle

Cowslips(left) and Yellow Rattle(right) flourish in meadows which have escaped the plough and chemicals. Other wildflowers such as the Southern Marsh Orchid (below) grow in wetter areas.
Butterflies of the brown family, such as the Marbled White (opposite), are typical of the meadows.

WOODLAND

The rich groundflora of the ancient woodlands provides a splash of spring colour. Yellow Archangel, Bluebell and Moschatel may all be found. Mosses, lichens and insects abound, especially in oak woodland where the attractive Oak Bush-cricket searches for insect prey. Many birds nest here, including the Great Spotted Woodpecker which is often seen and heard amongst the branches.

Below: Bluebells Inset: Oak Bush-cricket

Left: Great Spotted Woodpecker
Below: Yellow Archangel
Bottom: Primrose

Demoiselle Agrion

Kingfisher

RIVERS

The Brown Trout symbolizes the great attraction of Dorset's rivers to both fisherman and naturalist. A diverse vegetation includes the Yellow Water-lily, while the specialized Golden-ringed Dragonfly and Demoiselle Agrion breed amongst the clear waters. The Kingfisher is the most famous and colourful of the river birds.

Right: Golden-ringed Dragonfly Inset: Brown Trout Below: Yellow Water-lily

Sea Bindweed

SAND

Sand is Dorset's best-known asset and it attracts a particular range of wildlife, as well as the tourists. Strandline debris reveals the wealth of life around the shore, while in the dunes Marram Grass and flowers such as Sea Bindweed survive in the rather hostile, dry environment.

SHINGLE

Shifting pebbles and salty water make life difficult, but Chesil Beach has an interesting array of specialized plants such as Sea Kale and Sea Campion. The shingle is also used for nesting by birds such as the rare Little Tern.

Above: Sea Campion
Left: Little Tern
Main Picture: Sea Kale

Wild Cabbage

CLIFFS

This dramatic interface between land and sea is home to many plants and birds. Dorset boasts a range of cliff types from low, crumbling clays to massive, resistant limestones which support important colonies of seabirds such as Guillemots and Kittiwakes. Amongst the flowers clinging tenaciously to the rock faces are Wild Cabbage, Golden Samphire and Thrift.

Guillemots

Above: Golden Samphire
Main picture: Kittiwakes

COASTAL WATERS

While Dorset's coastal reedbeds are famous for their warblers, the Fleet and the two great natural harbours at Poole and Christchurch are important for waders and wildfowl such as Black-tailed Godwit and Brent Goose.

Black-tailed Godwit

Brent Geese

SIX

SAND AND SHINGLE

SAND IS ONE OF DORSET'S BEST-KNOWN ASSETS, at least as far as the tourist is concerned. From the miles of sandy beaches backed by a fascinating dune system at Studland, to the developed stretches of shore at Bournemouth, Swanage, Weymouth and the other holiday resorts, the sand and sea attract more people to the county than any other feature.

Left: Chesil Beach viewed from the Isle of Portland.

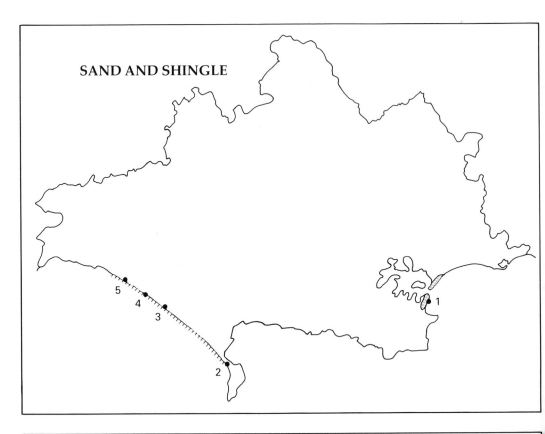

SAND AND SHINGLE

Key to map

⌂ Chesil Beach   ▨ Dunes   ● Places to visit

Site	Ownership	Main interest
1. Studland	National Trust/ Nature Conservancy Council	Plants, insects
2. Ferrybridge	Weymouth and Portland Borough Council	Insects, plants, birds
3. Abbotsbury	Private (Heritage Coast Project Car Park)	Plants
4. West Bexington	Private (Heritage Coast Project Car Park)	Plants
5. Burton Bradstock	National Trust	Plants

Strand-line

Behind the obvious human attraction, the sand forms important habitats which support a very particular range of wildlife. Invaded regularly by the ocean and always short of fresh water, the foreshore is a hostile environment for life. At low tide, observant naturalists notice some of the animals which do manage to overcome the problems. Polychaete worms – the sea fishermen's favourite bait – abound, though the only evidence of their presence when the tide is out are the casts formed by burrowers such as the Lugworm and the tubes of others like the Sand Mason. Cast-up shells of Tellin, Queen and Variegated Scallops and the introduced Slipper Limpet are further evidence of seashore life. Shell collectors' hauls at Shell Bay, Studland may also include Cockle, Mussel, Common Whelk, Common Otter Shell, Grooved Razor and Warty Venus.

The strand-line debris often includes dislodged seaweeds and curious 'mermaids' purses', actually the egg cases of skates and dogfish. White spongy balls are the massed egg cases of the common whelk. Cuttlefish 'bones', a favourite budgerigar titbit, are frequently cast ashore. These are the internal skeletons of a mollusc closely related to the squid which is quite common in the weedy shallows offshore. Masked, Shore and Hermit Crabs can also be found amongst the detritus and, together with other dead animals such as Sea Squirts, are valuable meat for scavengers such as Turnstone, Jackdaw and Carrion Crow.

Sand Dunes

Where the beach is shallowly sloping and relatively undisturbed, plants may become established beyond the reach of all but the highest tides. Sea Rocket, Sea Sandwort, Sea Lyme-grass and Sand Couch are typical of this habitat. When

Left: The dunes at Studland.

the wind blows onshore the developing plants trap small quantities of sand, forming little mounds. In time further growth raises the level of the beach locally and the process of dune formation has begun.

The dune system at Studland is one of the most remarkable and has been intensively studied by geomorphologists and ecologists for many years. Early-seventeenth-century maps show just a narrow spit of the Bagshot Beds with a low cliff facing the sea roughly in the position now occupied by the toll road. Sand accretion must have started around this time, and dune formation progressed quickly. By the mid-eighteenth century a third line of dunes was already forming. Today five dune ridges can be clearly identified, and though human pressures and the weather constantly threaten erosion, there are signs at various places on the foreshore of the beginnings of a new line of dunes.

Right: Sheep's-bit.

The main agent of dune development is Marram Grass. This remarkable plant takes on the building role once the incipient dune has been raised above the level where it is susceptible to inundation by the sea. Marram has the ability to grow up quickly through accumulating sand, building and securing the dune as it grows. A thick, waxy cuticle and a habit of curling its leaves to protect the leaf pores from drying winds, enable it to retain the meagre amounts of moisture obtained from deep within the free-draining sand. At a more superficial level the process of stabilization is helped by the growth of Sand Sedge and other specialized plants such as the rare Dune Fescue.

The blown sand which forms the Purbeck dunes is derived from eroded Tertiary sands and gravels, and is therefore unusually acid. Furthermore, the wave action in Studland Bay is very weak, so vacated shells on the sea bed and strand-line tend to remain unbroken and do not get blown inland. Hence the sand is also deficient in the shelly material which generally imparts a calcareous nature to dunes. This chemistry encourages a unique assemblage of plants amongst the Marram. Wildflowers include Sea Bindweed and the dandelion-like Cat's-ear. The attractive blue Sheep's-bit, an excellent indicator of acid soils, is also locally common here.

As the beach level continues to rise and a new line of dunes begins to form, the older dunes are slowly stabilized by the plants growing on them. The droppings and remains of herbivorous insects and mammals, and dead organic matter from lichens, grasses and other pioneers gradually accumulate, forming a primitive acid soil which encourages the growth of a mantle of heathers and gorse. This fixed dune vegetation grades almost imperceptibly into the heathland growing on the *in situ* Bagshot sands further inland.

Between the lines of dunes damp hollows – or slacks – support a rich variety of plants, including

Left: Female Bog Bush-cricket, green variety.

Marsh Orchids, Royal Fern, Sallow and Cross-leaved Heath. Little Sea at Studland, a freshwater lake created when the dune formation dammed a natural outlet, supports many of the typical emergent wet slack plants and rarities such as Six-stemmed Waterwort and Spring Quillwort.

The dry, hostile conditions on the sand and dunes do not at first sight seem particularly likely to support much animal life. Some insects thrive under these conditions, however, especially where the surface has achieved some stability. The diminutive Mottled Grasshopper sings its lively chirping song on the fixed dunes, gradually increasing the volume until a crescendo is reached. It may attract the attention of predatory Sand Lizards, which are as numerous as their Common relatives in places. Adders, Rabbits, Foxes and Woodmice inhabit the heathy parts in particular. Slacks attract Bog Bush-crickets, which can be found in a dull brown and

Right: The camouflaged nest of an Oystercatcher.

a much brighter emerald green form. Meadow Grasshoppers are very common in lush grassy parts of the marshy slacks, and permanent water provides breeding areas for a wide range of dragonflies and damselflies as well as amphibians such as the Toad.

Little Sea has the added bonus of breeding wildfowl. In winter numbers are swollen by Scaup, Pochard, Gadwall, Goldeneye and others. The shoreline also attracts some winter visitors. Sunbathing tourists are then replaced by Sanderling, Dunlin, Ringed Plover and Oystercatchers. In the dunes, resident Skylark and Meadow Pipit may be joined during spring and autumn passage by rarities like the Lapland Bunting. The beach also provides good views of wintering Brent Geese just offshore, occasionally accompanied by wildfowl such as Merganser, Common Scoter and Eider Duck. Studland Bay is a particularly popular area with grebes and at least three species, the Great-crested, Black-necked and Slavonian, can be seen most winters.

Shingle

Shingle habitat is rather more localized, both nationally and within the county. Chesil Beach, a fine example of a linear storm beach, is Dorset's prime shingle area. Stretching from the Isle of Portland westwards for 28 kilometres and varying in width from 150 to 200 metres, the beach is remarkable for the grading of pebble size, from pea-sized gravel at its western end to coarse rounded stones at Portland. Together with the associated Fleet, a tidal lagoon trapped behind the shingle bar, Chesil is a site of international importance for nature conservation.

At the sea's edge the relentless shifting of stones prevents plants from becoming established. A few ephemeral annuals such as Babington's Orache germinate and grow quickly on the strand-line, thanks to the locally rich nutrient supply derived from rotting seaweed. Their strategy is to use the relatively calm summer period to complete a life cycle and seed, before the storms of autumn completely destroy their foothold. To the landward side of the beach there is more stability and a remoteness from all but the most severe storm-driven high tides. Here there is a highly specialized and characteristic flora, well adapted to the lack of fresh water, the shifting substrate and salty winds. The glossy-leaved Sea Kale, Sea Pea, Sea Holly, Sea Campion and Shrubby Seablite occur locally, together with perhaps the best known and most attractive of shingle flowers, the Yellow-horned Poppy. In common with all legumes, the Sea Pea

Left: Sea Kale on Chesil Beach.

Scaly Crickets:
Right female, Left male.

bears root nodules inhabited by bacteria which are capable of fixing nitrogen from the air. The plant's share of this free fertilizer gives it a particular advantage in this low-nutrient environment, and it is dominant in localized areas.

Shingle plants avoid excessive water loss by several mechanisms. Most have a waxy waterproof cuticle, and the short, needle-like leaves of the Shrubby Seablite are also designed to conserve moisture. The tangled matted roots of these species are woody and resistant to the friction of the shifting pebbles. Their presence gradually helps to protect the stabilized shingle from the forces of the sea, allowing a range of other plants to become established. The community is, however, extremely sensitive to trampling and is easily damaged in areas of vehicular access or intense recreational pressure.

The unstable and inhospitable shingle habitat is not associated with a rich fauna, but invertebrates such as Sea Slaters may be found, and at one point on Chesil Beach there is the only British colony of the curious Scaly Cricket, though its origins are uncertain. The beach is most important for a breeding colony of Little Tern, well protected from human disturbance during the nesting season, but still rather susceptible to predators such as Foxes, gulls and rats. Lapwing, Ringed Plover, Redshank and Oystercatcher also breed along the beach where it forms the shore of the Fleet. In winter, Snow Buntings are regular visitors.

Visiting the Beaches

Most of Dorset's beaches can be visited, though vehicle access is not always easy. Studland is in the ownership of the National Trust and most of the dune system is leased to the Nature Conservancy Council as a National Nature Reserve. The area is particularly susceptible to erosion, so paths and marked nature trails must be followed and areas of dune restoration avoided. Much of Chesil Beach is in private ownership and access is less simple. At Ferrybridge, on the road to Portland, a car park includes visitor information and a trail to the crest of the shingle beach. Further west the beach is accessible at various points including Abbotsbury, West Bexington and Burton Bradstock. The habitat here is also sensitive to pressures, and cars should not be driven off the surfaced roads.

CHECKLIST OF TYPICAL SAND DUNE AND SHINGLE BEACH PLANTS AND ANIMALS

Wildflowers

Sea Bindweed   *Calystegia soldanella*
Sheep's-bit   *Jasione montana*

Yellow-horned Poppy   *Glaucium flavum*
Sea Kale   *Crambe maritima*

Grasses

Marram   *Ammophila arenaria*
Sea Lyme Grass   *Leymus arenarius*

Insects

Mottled Grasshopper   *Myrmeleotettix maculatus*

Birds

Meadow Pipit   *Anthus pratensis*

Little Tern   *Sterna albifrons*
Oystercatcher   *Haematopus ostralegus*

Reptiles

Sand Lizard   *Lacerta agilis*

Sea Rocket

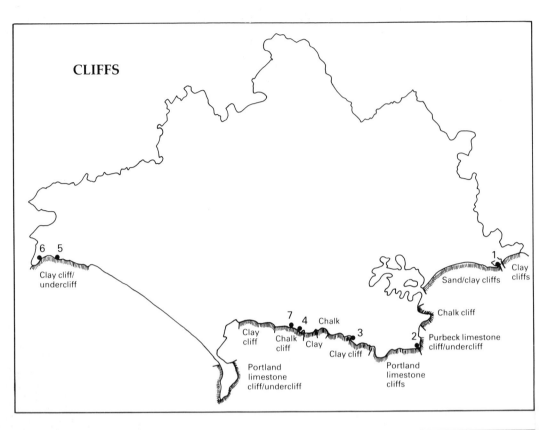

CLIFFS

Clay cliff/undercliff

6 5

Sand/clay cliffs

1

Clay cliffs

Chalk cliff

7 4 Chalk

Clay cliff

Chalk cliff

Clay

3

2

Purbeck limestone cliff/undercliff

Clay cliff

Portland limestone cliff/undercliff

Portland limestone cliffs

Key to map

▨ Cliffs

● Places to visit

Site	Ownership	Main interest
1. Hengistbury Head	Bournemouth Borough Council	Plants, geology
2. Durlston Country Park	Dorset County Council	Plants, birds, insects
3. Kimmeridge	Private	Plants, geology
4. Lulworth Cove	Private	Plants, geology
5. Charmouth	Charmouth Parish Council (Car Park)	Geology
6. Lyme Regis	West Dorset District Council (Car Parks)	Geology, plants
7. Durdle Door	Private	Geology

SEVEN

CLIFFS

NOTHING IS MORE EXHILARATING THAN A VISIT to Dorset's cliffs on a stormy day.
Waves crashing on the rocks, relentless gales whipping up mists of salty sea spray,
and seabirds passing close inshore to make the most of what little shelter the
coastline is able to offer, are all enduring memories.

The Purbeck cliffs from St
Aldhelm's Head.

Above: Charmouth beach and Golden Cap.

A t such times this dramatic interface between the land and the sea can seem extremely inhospitable for wildlife, yet on calm summer days, when tufts of Thrift decorate the rocks and the cries of Kittiwakes fill the air, there are few places so peaceful and relaxing and so rich in plant, insect and bird life. The cliffs in all their contrasting guises are most rewarding places for a naturalist to visit.

The diverse geology of the Dorset coastline has created a variety of cliff types. The generally softer rocks of the extreme west of the county slump under the influence of both the sea and the waters draining off the land, to form large and rather mobile areas of undercliff and landslip. At Charmouth, the orange sandstones which give Golden Cap its name crown the highest cliff on the south coast. Lower down the 189-metre rock face, the underlying clays and shales are rich in fossils, like so many of the sedimentary rocks which form the coastline.

Further east the Isle of Portland stretches out into the Channel, its stubborn and resilient limestone cliffs defying the powers of the ocean. Fallen boulders litter the shoreline in parts, the products of natural erosion often supplemented by many centuries of quarrying activity. Here another type of undercliff forms, much more stable and supporting a highly structured and more permanent vegetation. Beyond Portland, the gleaming white walls of chalk form a decorative backdrop to the seaside town of Weymouth.

The sheer Portland limestone of Purbeck is popular with seabirds and climbers alike. Natural caves along the base of the cliffs are dwarfed in places by quarries driven deep into the face. The intricate detail of the many strata included in the Purbeck limestone beds are revealed in the cliffs of Durlston Bay south of Swanage. To the north of the town the chalk cliffs reappear, dropping vertically to the sea and eroding unevenly to form the strange arches and pinnacles at Old Harry Rocks.

The cliffs at the eastern end of Dorset may be the least dramatic, but they too have a special character and wildlife value. A few remnants of heather-clothed slopes remind visitors to the vast conurbation of Poole and Bournemouth of the natural vegetation of the cliffs here before it was largely replaced with concrete, pleasure gardens and pine trees. Hengistbury Head stands like a sentinel on the shores of Christchurch Harbour, while to the east are low, crumbling cliffs which stretch across the county boundary to the Hampshire seaside towns of Barton and Milford. These form yet another unique feature of interest to the geologist and ecologist.

The remarkable flora and fauna of the Dorset cliffs is a reflection not only of the geology but also the favourable south-coast climate, and the year-round protection from frost that a seaside location bestows. Other influences determining which plants and animals will succeed here include a paucity of soil, regular inundation with salt spray and an often precarious position.

Left: Cliffs at Kimmeridge.

Above: Long-winged Conehead.

Clay and Shale

Unstable clay and shale cliffs occur at places along the coast. The associated landslips, mudflows and undercliff are typified by the area around Lyme Regis. Plants cannot get a foothold on mobile areas but once they start to stabilize, if only temporarily, Coltsfoot is often the first plant to appear. The open conditions of such landslips favour certain specialized insects, particularly where a southerly aspect encourages even greater warmth in the summer. The Grey Bush-cricket, a normally rare insect, can occur in large colonies at locations where there are patches of bare ground suitable for egg laying, interspersed with refuges of tussocky vegetation which provide food and shelter from predators. Its dependence on high summer temperatures and frost-free winters means that the species is almost totally restricted to a narrow band along the extreme southern coast.

The community of grasses, bramble and bracken which develops on these unstable cliffs gives way in time to a scrub community, rich in insect life. The impressive Great Green Bush-cricket is typical of these areas, its loud, far-carrying rattle sounding throughout the afternoon and evening on warm late summer evenings. Where the ground remains wet a marsh vegetation develops. Marsh orchids, including the Marsh Helleborine, Brooklime, Ragged Robin and Water Mint are all found in such areas, usually with stands of rushes and sedges. Near Chapman's Pool, marshy slips are home to colonies of the Long-winged Conehead, a once extremely rare relative of the grasshopper, which has greatly extended its range along the Dorset coast since the early 1970s.

Where the landslips remain stable, woodland may eventually develop. Scrubby Oak, Holly and Sycamore shade out the existing flora, which is replaced with typical coastal Dorset plants such as Stinking Iris, Hartstongue and Bluebells. These woodlands give cover to Roe Deer, Badger and Fox and provide a welcome landfall for the vast legions of small birds arriving on Dorset's shores during the spring migration.

The cliffs formed by the Kimmeridge clays tend to be relatively stable, and a characteristic community of Sea Campion, Wild Cabbage and Thrift develops. The low clay cliffs of the east of the county are colonized by less specialized flowers, many of which occur in a variety of coastal habitats. Sea Beet and Buck's-horn Plantain are two typical examples.

Chalk and Limestone

The chalk and limestone cliffs of Dorset support a rich and diverse range of plants and animals. The natural rock garden of the limestone includes Thrift, Rock Samphire, Golden Samphire, Rock Sea-lavender and Sea Plantain. The clifftop grasslands boast many of the typical downland flowers and grasses, supplemented by salt-tolerant species such as Buck's-horn Plantain, Sea Campion and the Common and Early Scurvy-grass. The fleshy grey leaves of many of these plants are an excellent adaptation for survival in this often harsh, salty environment.

The undercliffs of Portland and Durlston Bay have an almost Mediterranean feel to the vegetation. Exotic Red Valerian flowers profusely amongst the boulders in a matrix of grassland and scrub. Marjoram, Wild Madder, Herb Robert, Wood Sage, Stinking Iris and several Broomrapes – most notably the Ivy Broomrape – add to the interest. Honeysuckle, Ivy and Old Man's Beard scramble decoratively over a range of shrubs, including the native Wild Privet and Wayfaring Tree, while Adders, Foxes and Kestrels hunt for the abundant small mammal and invertebrate prey.

Other typical plants of the chalk and limestone clifftops sound like escapes from the vegetable garden. Wild Carrot, Cabbage, Sea Beet and Black Mustard may often be found in close proximity, and the gardener may take some consolation from the discovery that most of the Wild Cabbage plants become infested with the caterpillars of the Large White butterfly as well!

Many of Dorset's cliff plants are very local or

Left: Thrift growing on the cliffs at Anvil Point.

rare. In some years, particularly those when the Purbeck cliffs show a magnificent display of Wild Carrot, the strange, parasitic Carrot Broomrape is a frequent sight. The coastal downlands here are also the stronghold of the Early Spider Orchid, but for rarities the cliffs of Portland are quite outstanding. In addition to over two hundred types of lichen and several very unusual mosses such as *Eurhynchium meridionale*, the area supports Portland Spurge, Hoary Stock and the endemic Portland Sea-lavender.

Even within Purbeck there is considerable variation amongst the wildflowers, reflecting local changes in the geology of the clifftops. At St Aldhelms Head the Portland stone alone forms the exposure, and Viper's Bugloss is a common sight along the clifftop Coast Path in the summer. Further east towards Durlston Country Park, the Portland limestone is topped with Purbeck limestone and the same plant is very rarely encountered. The distribution of Rock-rose, Harebell and Betony is likewise strongly affected along the coast. The clifftop chalk grassland also has its specialities. Many, like the Nottingham Catchfly, are absent or less common on the limestone.

Many of the typical downland insects spread down to the clifftop. Butterflies include Small Blues, often to be seen laying their pale blue eggs amongst the flowers of the Kidney Vetch, and that great Dorset speciality, the Lulworth Skipper, a small and rather drab butterfly which occurs in great numbers along sections of the Purbeck Coast. The Green Hairstreak is often encountered where European Gorse forms clifftop scrub, and Marbled White and Dark Green Fritillary are also quite common. Other insects include several species of Bush-cricket and the native Lesser Cockroach. The limestone and mild climate combine to create ideal conditions for many species of snail, many of which are very rare elsewhere in Britain.

Undoubtedly the most spectacular members of the coastal community, the seabirds find nest sites on many of the more inaccessible, stable and precipitous cliffs. Some of the chalk provides a foothold for small colonies, including Cormorant and Great Black-backed Gull, but the Portland limestone cliffs between Durlston Head and St Aldhelms Head hold greater numbers. These are small colonies by the standards of northern Britain but they are nevertheless extremely important because of their geographical location.

Near to sea level, Shags form rough nests of weed on wide ledges and platforms, risking inundation by the tide and consequent loss of the nest and eggs. Sitting low in the water or perched with wings outstretched to dry their non-waterproofed feathers, Shags are often mistaken for their close relative, the Cormorant, but they can be distinguished by a breeding season crest and the lack of white at the base of the beak and on the thigh.

Guillemots crowd together on narrow ledges and in nooks and crannies to lay their pear-shaped eggs – an adaptation which helps to prevent them rolling off the ledge when blown about or accidentally knocked. By their sixteenth day the chicks are ready for the sea, and flutter or bounce down to begin an oceanic life broken only

Right: Lulworth Skipper.

Left: Puffin.

briefly each year for breeding. Early escape to the sea helps to protect the chicks from predators: despite the apparent inaccessibility of the nest, marauding gulls take their toll of eggs and young and even land predators such as Stoats have been recorded scaling the cliffs in search of a meal.

The less numerous Razorbill lays a single egg in fissures or behind small boulders on the cliff face. A third member of the auk family, the Puffin, has declined drastically in numbers over recent decades. Usually nesting in rabbit bur-rows, disused badger setts and other soft earth at the top of the cliffs, the Puffin was particularly susceptible to disturbance by the increasing numbers of human visitors to the coast. The few pairs remaining have adapted to breed in caves and hollows in the cliff, usually nesting well out of sight behind boulders.

While the auks generally show a worrying downward trend, the opposite is true of other seabird numbers, particularly the Fulmar. Unknown in Dorset in Victorian times this tube-nose, a relative of the albatross, has steadily increased over recent years. This is particularly surprising in view of its low capacity for reproduction. Birds do not mature until about eight years of age and then only a single egg is laid each year. This has an unusually long, and hence hazardous, incubation period of around fifty days. The reason for the increase despite these apparent hindrances is probably the longevity of the Fulmar. Detailed studies by researchers suggest that birds attaining thirty years of age are not unusual and a proportion may live a good deal longer.

Amongst the cliff-nesting gulls, the Kittiwake is the most vociferous and attractive. The persistent cry of 'kitt-i-wake' from the colonies is the most typical sound on a visit to the Purbeck cliffs in the summer. It may be distinguished from its other common relatives not only by call but also by its black legs and solidly black wingtips.

Other birds which nest on the cliffs but which rely more on the land than the sea for their requirements include the Rock Pipit, Swift and Jackdaw. Starlings and Stock Doves may also

Right: Penn's Weare, Portland.

breed in places, and the chalk cliffs near Studland unusually support a colony of House Martins. Birds of prey are also represented though only the Kestrel is at all common. Once nesting in reasonable numbers but more recently decimated through persecution and pollution, the Peregrine is now showing promising signs of a comeback, again providing the fortunate birdwatcher with the ultimate thrill of observing a 'stoop' on a Feral Pigeon or Stock Dove along the cliffs. The signs for another impressive cliff nester, the Raven, are less encouraging. Although birds are occasionally seen passing along the coast there have been only a few positive signs of successful breeding for some years.

Seawatching

The clifftops are an excellent viewing point for watching migrant birds. Portland and Durlston have an envied reputation for providing views of all sorts of rarities. These include birds flying on or offshore during the spring and autumn migrations, and a huge range of seabirds, wildfowl and waders passing along the Channel at various times of the year. Seawatching can be a rewarding experience, though the best results are generally obtained in the worst weather. Gannets, Manx Shearwaters and various species of Skua are seen regularly, and a keen eye will occasionally pick out Common Scoter, grebes and divers. Marine mammals may also be seen close inshore. Bottle-nosed Dolphins are seen quite regularly, as are pods of Pilot Whales. Common and Risso's Dolphin have also been recorded around Weymouth and Portland harbours in recent times, and fishermen often report sightings of groups of Harbour Porpoise.

Visiting the Cliffs

While there are very few easy access points to the cliffs for vehicles, the coastal Long Distance Footpath follows the cliffs for much of its Dorset length and provides spectacular views and memorable experiences for the more adventurous. Car parks at Lyme Regis and Charmouth attract fossil hunters to the cliffs, though constant danger of cliff falls, and the damage which uncontrolled hammering can cause here and elsewhere along the coast, must be borne in mind. Short walks from the roads on Portland lead to the rich wildlife habitats of the undercliffs. The famous coastal features at Durdle Door and Lulworth Cove are easily seen by those willing to undertake a short walk from the respective car parks.

Access to the Purbeck cliffs is restricted to Kimmeridge Bay via a toll road and to Durlston Country Park at the Isle's south-east corner. Here there is an excellent park centre with information, displays and leaflets which include items about the cliffs. Waymarked paths include a clifftop trail which leads to Anvil Point Lighthouse and the main clifftop observation point where further panels help to identify and describe the nesting and passing birds.

CHECKLIST OF TYPICAL CLIFF PLANTS AND ANIMALS

Wildflowers

Thrift	*Armeria maritima*
Sea Campion	*Silene maritima*
Wild Cabbage	*Brassica oleracea*
Rock Samphire	*Crithmum maritimum*
Portland Spurge	*Euphorbia portlandica*
Common Scurvy-grass	*Cochlearia officinalis*

Insects

Small Blue	*Cupido minimus*
Grey Bush-cricket	*Platycleis albopunctata*

Birds

Fulmar	*Fulmarus glacialis*
Kittiwake	*Rissa tridactyla*
Guillemot	*Uria aalge*
Great Black-backed Gull	*Larus marinus*
Herring Gull	*Larus argentatus*

EIGHT

COASTAL WATERS

Left: Poole Harbour and the coast at Studland.
Above: The RSPB reserve at Radipole Lake.

Reedbeds

Brackish grassland and coastal reedbeds form some of Dorset's most famous birdwatching sites. Scarce breeding warblers and the ever present chance of a real rarity on passage are a great draw for ornithologists of all standards.

The best-known reedbeds are those of the nature reserves of the Royal Society for the Protection of Birds at Weymouth. At the heart of the built-up area, Radipole Lake and Lodmoor have survived various pressures and local developments and continue to provide excellent habitats for wildlife and, incidentally, marvellous opportunities for amateur naturalists. Similar habitats are found along the length of the county's coastline from the Stanpit Marsh Local Nature Reserve in Christchurch Harbour, to smaller riverside beds such as that behind the beach at Charmouth.

Although usually dominated by the Common

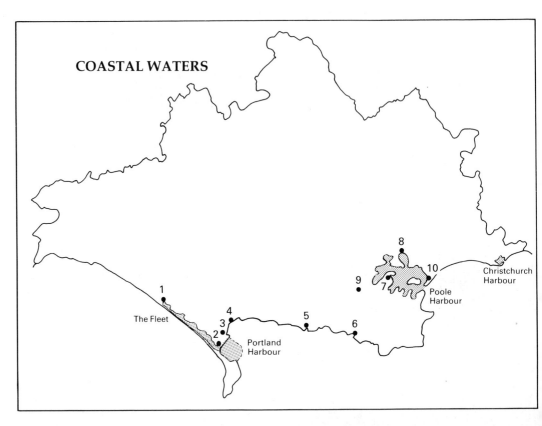

COASTAL WATERS

The Fleet

Portland
Harbour

Poole
Harbour

Christchurch
Harbour

Key to map

• Places to visit

Site	Ownership	Main attractions	Wildlife importance
1. Abbotsbury	Private*	Swannery, reed bed, Fleet	Birds, plants
2. Ferrybridge	Weymouth and Portland Borough Council/Crown Estate Commissioners	Chesil Beach, Fleet, Portland Harbour	Birds, plants, insects
3. Radipole Lake	Weymouth and Portland Borough Council/RSPB	Reed beds	Birds
4. Lodmoor			
5. Lulworth	Private	Marine life, geology	Marine life
6. Kimmeridge	Private*	Marine Nature Reserve	Marine life
7. Arne	RSPB	Poole Harbour	Birds, plants, insects
8. Upton Country Park	Poole Borough Council	Poole Harbour	Birds, plants, insects
9. Wareham Quay	Purbeck District Council/Private	Reed beds and saltmarsh	Birds, plants
10. Sandbanks	(Road)	Saltmarsh	Birds

* Entrance fee to some areas

Reed, the habitat also includes other plant species. Rushes, Reed Canary Grass and Pond Sedge are all widespread and in brackish conditions they are often joined by Sea Club-rush, Sea Milkwort and the more obvious and colourful Sea Aster – a native species rather similar to the related Michaelmas Daisy. Where the reedbeds grade into brackish grasslands the vegetation is composed of the typical Creeping Bent and Marsh Foxtail – often with Bulrush, Marsh Arrowgrass, Saltmarsh Rush and Strawberry Clover. At Arne, reedswamps often include Black Bog-rush and Blunt-flowered Rush.

Specialist insects include two members of the

grasshopper family, the Lesser Marsh Grasshopper and the Short-winged Conehead, both more often heard than seen. The Common Reed is the foodplant of several highly specialized moth caterpillars including the Large Wainscot and its rather scarce relative, the Flame Wainscot. It is for their year-round bird interest that the reeds are most famous, however.

In spring the large reedbeds along the coast come alive with the songs of warblers. Sedge and Reed Warblers are everywhere and in a few locations they are joined by the rare Cetti's Warbler. Marsh and Savi's Warblers are also

occasional nesters in the Weymouth area, while Bearded Tit and Reed Buntings – two other reedbed specialists – are amongst some fifty breeding species at Radipole.

Autumn brings huge pre-migration flocks of Martins and Swallows to the reedbeds, often with congregations of Yellow Wagtails. The autumn and spring passage also sees regular visits by waders common and uncommon, including Spotted Redshank, Wood and Green Sandpipers, Whimbrel and Ruff. Perhaps the most familiar reedbed birds are the ducks, but up to fifteen species of wildfowl are recorded each winter at Radipole, with wintering Heron, Pied Wagtail and Snipe swelling their respective resident populations. The less saline reedbeds also attract terns and gulls to bathe and drink and Radipole in particular is well-known for its attractiveness to rare species of these coastal birds.

Estuary and Saltmarsh

The two natural harbours at Poole and Christchurch support the main areas of saltmarsh and estuary life in Dorset. Further west the Fleet is a unique and diverse lagoon, saline at its mouth and grading to almost fresh water at its western and northern extremities around Abbotsbury.

With such a diversity of chemical and physical conditions, it is no surprise that the Fleet supports a plant, invertebrate and bird community of incredible complexity. Over 150 species of algae grow here, alongside Spiral and Beaked Tasselweeds and the Eelgrasses which feed the flocks of Brent Geese and other wildfowl.

Regular breeding birds of the Fleet include Shelduck, Mallard, Great Crested and Little Grebe and Coot, the latter the target of a traditional annual shoot. Several common waders also breed here, often nesting on the adjacent Chesil Beach, but the Fleet is perhaps most famous for the breeding Mute Swans at Abbots-

Left: Cetti's Warbler.

Right: Shelduck. Below: The
fleet from Ferrybridge.

bury's 900-year-old swannery. The hundred or so pairs are joined by winter visitors which swell the population to around a thousand birds by December.

The waters also support good numbers of wintering Wigeon, Teal, Pochard, Scaup, Gadwall, Pintail and Shoveler. To the seaward end of the lagoon Goldeneye, Red-breasted Merganser and Long-tailed Duck are also frequent visitors and in hard weather, Common and Velvet Scoter and Eider are occasionally seen. Low tide exposes mudflats which attract Dunlin, Curlew and Oystercatcher: the Fleet typically attracts a good range of waders – more than forty species have been recorded – though seldom in the spectacular numbers seen at other coastal sites. It is an excellent place to watch, not only for waders on passage, but also for birds of prey.

wildlife in the area. Artificially created to serve the needs of Her Majesty's Navy, the harbour sees three common Divers and five species of Grebe most winters, while the rocky sections of shoreline attract Purple Sandpiper and Turn-

stone. The little that is known about the intertidal and marine life of the harbour suggests that it is a very important site. It offers frequent opportunities to see marine mammals, with Common, Bottle-nosed and Risso's Dolphins recorded in recent years. Work here and on the Purbeck Marine Nature Reserve at Kimmeridge is indicating that the county's wildlife riches do not stop at the shoreline; much more research is necessary into the inshore waters off the Dorset coast to ensure the conservation of these largely unseen but equally important habitats.

More than twenty species of fish have been caught in the Fleet, from the more commercially important Mullet and Bass – for which the area is a vital nursery area – to the familiar Eel, Stickleback and Pipefish, a relative of the seahorse.

Between the mouth of the Fleet and the open sea, Portland Harbour provides sheltered water for many more birds, especially in the winter, adding to an already impressive variety of

By contrast, Poole Harbour has been intensively studied in connection with developments associated with the onshore oilfield of Purbeck. Detailed surveys of marine life and the saltmarsh communities have revealed a habitat of very high productivity dominated by worms and bristleworms, the sea angler's favourite bait. While some parts show reduced diversity due to pollution, others are still quite clean and support a good diversity of life.

Rare species, many confined to this immediate

area, are being found as knowledge accumulates and research continues. Commercial fisheries of native shellfish – Oysters, Mussels and Clams – are dependent on the Harbour as are sea fish such as Salmon, Trout and Eels. Mullet, Bass, Flounder, Sole and Plaice are also landed and parts of the harbour are nursery areas for Herring, Bass and Flounder.

The fish are the main predators of invertebrates when the tide is in, but twice a day parts of the bed are exposed to form mudflats, which offer the wading birds an opportunity to search out the same prey. The range of food items on offer depends on the coarseness of the sediment, the quality of the water and the location relative to the main channels. This determines the length and frequency of exposure and the current strength when the tide is in. Generally, the finer and more mobile sediments support fewer organisms. Sandy areas are rich in worms and snails while gravel and rocks offer a more permanent reliable home to Shore Crabs, Mussels, various barnacles, anemones, sponges and seaweeds.

Each of the predatory birds has a highly adapted bill and feeding mechanism which has evolved to cope with a specific section of the diverse invertebrate community. The long, curved bill of the Curlew is perfect for extracting the bristleworms (such as the Lugworm) from their burrows, which may be up to 20 cm deep. The sturdy bill of the Oystercatcher is used to probe for Tellins and other shellfish, and if necessary, has the power to break the larger shells and extract the creature from within. The staple diet of the shorter-billed Plovers is the Laver Spire Shell which is found at or near the surface of the mudflats. The aptly named Turnstone does just that – searching for crabs and other mobile creatures which have taken

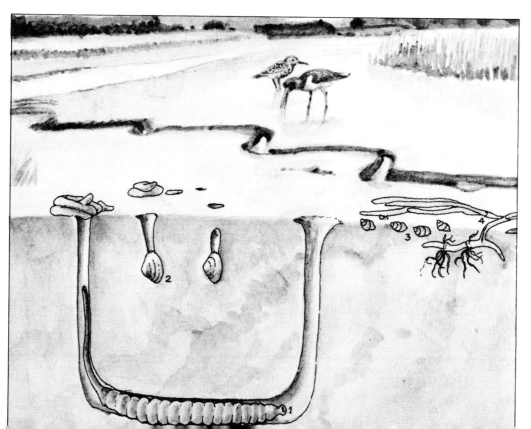

Mudflat life.

1. Lugworm 2. Tellin ((Macoma) 3. Laver spire shell (Hydrobia) 4. Eelgrass.

refuge beneath small rocks whilst the tide is out.

The wintering bird community of Poole and Christchurch Harbours includes congregations of Shelduck, Black-tailed Godwit and Oystercatcher which are of international significance. Redshank, Snipe, Curlew, Ruff and Dunlin also occur in good numbers. The lagoon on Brownsea Island supports Avocet and is frequently visited by Spotted Redshank. With a large heronry, and breeding Common and Sandwich Tern, the

Below: Sea Lavender, Poole Harbour

Island is an important Nature Reserve. Wintering Brent Geese and Wigeon are joined over much of Poole Harbour by a variety of wildfowl, grebes, divers and the Red-breasted Merganser.

Most of the Dorset saltmarsh is dominated by Townsend's Cord-grass, an artificial hybrid between a native and an alien Spartina species. At one time threatening to swamp all other intertidal areas, the grass is now dying back in some areas. Spartina beds are not widely used by birds, though Redshank may roost in some areas. Drain edges support a wider variety of plants, including Sea Purslane, English Scurvy-grass and Annual Seablite.

The curious Glasswort grows on open muddy areas and the higher, drier saltmarsh comprises Saltmarsh Grass, Sea Arrowgrass, Sea Plantain, Sea Aster, Sea Rush and Sea Clubrush. Sea Lavender forms decorative and quite extensive beds in sheltered parts. All of these species must tolerate high levels of salt to survive, and show adaptations such as fleshy leaves and waxy cuticles which help to conserve fresh water within the plant.

Visiting the Coastal Waters

The RSPB nature reserves at Radipole and Lodmoor are excellent, not only for birds but also for birdwatchers. The Fleet can be viewed from Chesil Beach at Ferrybridge where the local authority provides a car park and information beside the road across to Portland. This is also a good place to watch Portland Harbour. Other lengths of the shore of both water bodies are accessible from the coastal footpaths.

Most of the undeveloped stretches of Poole Harbour's coastline are impossible to reach. However excellent viewing facilities are provided from a hide at the Arne nature reserve of the RSPB (proving the all-round attraction of this area which has so much more than just heathland interest) and at Upton Country Park. Pleasant walks from the area of the quay at Wareham also give good views of the reedbeds and saltmarsh; for the less energetic it is possible to park right beside the mudflats at Sandbanks on the Poole side of the harbour, near to the Ferry to Studland. Here, especially in the winter, it is possible to obtain excellent views of wildfowl and waders.

The adventurous will not wish to miss a boat trip to Brownsea Island, a nature reserve of the Dorset Trust for Nature Conservation. Trips can be arranged from Poole Quay and from Sandbanks.

CHECKLIST OF TYPICAL PLANTS AND ANIMALS FROM THE COASTAL WATERS

Wildflowers

Sea Aster   *Aster tripolium*
Sea Purslane   *Halimione portulacoides*
Sea Lavender   *Limonium vulgare*

Insects

Lesser Marsh
  Grasshopper   *Chorthippus albomarginatus*

Birds

Redshank   *Tringa totanus*
Oystercatcher   *Haematopus ostralegus*
Shelduck   *Tadorna tadorna*

Mute Swan   *Cygnus olor*
Brent Goose   *Branta bernicla*
Wigeon   *Anas penelope*
Reed Warbler   *Acrocephalus scirpaceus*
Reed Bunting   *Emberiza schoeniclus*

Fish

Bass   *Dicentrarchus labrax*
Mullet   *Mugil chelo*

Rock-pool life.

Left to right: Serrated wrack, Anemone: Beadlet, Snakelocks, Shore Crab, Mussels.

APPENDIX 1
Useful Addresses

Avon Forest Park
Barnsfield Visitor Centre
St Leonards
Near Ringwood
Hampshire
Tel: 04254 78470

British Butterfly Conservation Society
Tudor House
Quorn
Loughborough
Leicestershire LE12 8AD

**British Herpetological Society and
Herpetological Conservation Trust**
Dorset Contact: 0202 524035

**British Trust for Conservation
Volunteers**
Dorset Office: 0305 267581

Dorset Badger Group
Dorset Bat Group
via DTNC Conservation Office
Half Moon House
North Square
Dorchester

Dorset Environmental Records Centre
Colliton House Annexe
Glyde Path Road
Dorchester
Tel: 0305 204281

**Dorset Natural History and
Archaeology Society**
c/o Dorset County Museum
High West Street
Dorchester
Tel: 0305 262735

Dorset Trust for Nature Conservation
39 Christchurch Road
Bournemouth
BH1 3NS
Tel: 0202 24241

Durlston Country Park
Swanage
BH19 2JL
Tel: 0929 424443

Forestry Commission
Dorset Forest Office
Coldharbour
Wareham
Tel: 0929 551811

The National Trust
Wessex Regional Office
Stourton
Warminster
Wiltshire
Tel: 0747 840224

**Royal Society for the Protection
of Birds**
South West Regional Office
10 Richmond Road
Exeter
Devon
EX4 4JA
Tel: 0392 432691

APPENDIX 2
Further Reading and References

Birds of Dorset Boys, J.V. & Prendergast,
E.D.V. (David & Charles, 1983)

Butterflies of Dorset Thomas, J. & Webb, N.R.
(Dorset Natural History and Archaeology
Society, 1984)

Coastal Studies in Purbeck Canning, A.D. &
Maxted, K.R. (Purbeck Press, 1979)

A Concise Flora of Dorset Good, R. (Dorset
Natural History and Archaeology
Society, 1984)

Field Studies; Purbeck Taverner, J. (Focal Point
Audio-Visual, 1981)

Wildflowers of Dorset Roberts, S. (Dovecot
Press, 1984)

GENERAL INDEX

Page numbers in italic refer to illustrations.

SPECIES INDEX

Page numbers in italic refer
to illustrations.